Longman Science for AQA

GCSE Extension Units

Series Editor: **Nigel English**

Muriel Claybrook
Rich
Penn
Su
Penny

PEARSON
Longman
Edinburgh Gate
Harlow, Essex

This book also includes

Active Book

How to use this book

This book is divided into three parts, B3 (Biology), C3 (Chemistry) and P3 (Physics). Each of these parts is divided into two units. Each unit has a one-page introduction and is then divided into topics. At the end of each unit there are some practice coursework questions, and at the end of each part there is a set of assessment questions that will help you practise for your exams and a glossary of key words.

As well as the paper version of the book there is a CD-ROM called an ActiveBook. For more information on the ActiveBook please see the next two pages.

What to look for on the pages of this book:

Learning objectives
These tell you what you should know after you have studied the topic.

Questions
There are lots of questions to help you think about the main points in each topic.

Glossary words
You will need to know the meaning of some key words. These are shown in **bold**. The glossary at the end of each part gives you a list of all the key words and what they mean.

B3.11
Dialysis treatment

By the end of this topic you should be able to:

- describe how a person with kidney failure may be treated with dialysis and explain why it has to be carried out at regular intervals
- describe how substances are exchanged between dialysis fluid and the patient's blood across partially permeable membranes to restore normal levels in the blood
- evaluate the advantages and disadvantages of dialysis treatment.

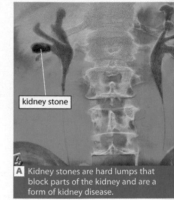

kidney stone

A Kidney stones are hard lumps that block parts of the kidney and are a form of kidney disease.

Many people have kidney disease, sometimes without even knowing it. Many things can cause it, such as infection, diabetes, long-term high blood pressure or damage in an accident. The treatment offered by a doctor will depend on the cause of the disease.

1 Suggest why people can have kidney disease without knowing it.

2 Explain why a stone blocking the ureter could affect how a kidney works.

Only a small proportion of people with kidney disease will eventually develop **kidney failure**. This is defined as occurring when less than 30% of the kidneys function properly. At this stage the body can be affected badly by the lack of kidney function.

3 a Explain as fully as you can what will happen to the concentration of substances in the blood if the kidneys are failing.
  b Suggest what effect this will have on the cells in the body.

One way of treating kidney failure is **haemodialysis**. This is when a machine takes over the function of the kidneys. Needles are inserted into blood vessels, often in the patient's arm. Blood flows from the patient through a tube to the machine and is returned through another tube. Inside the machine the blood flows through a filter called a **dialyser**.

Inside the dialyser, a partially permeable membrane separates the blood from the dialysing fluid. This fluid contains the right proportions of substances to allow diffusion of waste products, such as urea and excess substances, out of the blood. It also ensures that glucose and useful mineral ions aren't lost from the blood during dialysis.

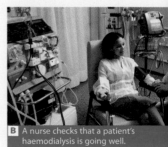

B A nurse checks that a patient's haemodialysis is going well.

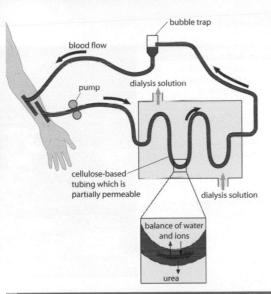

- bubble trap
- blood flow
- pump
- dialysis solution
- cellulose-based tubing which is partially permeable
- dialysis solution
- balance of water and ions
- urea

C Diffusion into and out of the blood happens in a dialyser just like in the kidney.

4 **a** Explain how the dialyser mimics the normal function of the kidney.

H **b** In what way does the dialyser *not* mimic the normal function of the kidney?

D Peritoneal dialysis uses a natural membrane in the abdomen as the dialysis membrane.

How good is dialysis?

Dialysis only partly copies the action of the kidney. So people with kidney failure also need to control their diet to prevent a build-up of particular substances, and to avoid taking in too much fluid. Peritoneal dialysis is done continually and you can move around at the same time, but the patient and family have to be careful to carry out the dialysis properly. Haemodialysis is usually done three times a week, for about four hours each time, and often in hospital with supervision. Without treatment, a patient with kidney failure would eventually fall into a coma and die from the toxins in the blood or from a heart attack.

5 Describe **one** advantage of using dialysis to treat kidney failure.

6 Make a list of the disadvantages of using dialysis for treating kidney failure.

7 Write a brief article for a website that explains to kidney disease patients how dialysis is used to treat these patients.

How to use your ActiveBook

The ActiveBook is an electronic copy of the book, which you can use on a compatible computer. The CD-ROM will only play while the disc is in the computer. The ActiveBook has these features:

Glossary
Click this tab to see all of the key words and what they mean. You can read them or you can click 'play' and listen to someone else read them out for you to help with the pronunciation.

DigiList
Click on this tab and all the electronic files on the ActiveBook will be listed in menus.

ActiveBook tab
Click this tab to access the electronic copy of the book.

Key words
Click on any of the words in **bold** to see a box with the word and what it means. You can read it or you can click 'play' and listen to someone else read it out for you to help with the pronunciation.

Interactive view
Click this button to see all the bits on the page that link to electronic files. You have access to all of the features that are useful for you to use at home on your own. If you don't want to see these links you can return to **Book view**.

ActiveBook   DigiList   bc Glossary

P3.4 Circular motion

By the end of this topic you should be able to:
- identify which forces provide the centripetal force in a given situation
- interpret data on bodies moving in circular paths
- recall that when a body moves in a circle, it continuously accelerates towards the centre of the circle
- describe what centripetal force is, and in which direction it acts
- explain how the centripetal force changes if the mass or speed of the body changes, or if the radius of the circle changes.

You may not think of a motorbike going round a bend at a constant speed as accelerating, but it is! **Acceleration** is a change in **velocity**, and velocity depends on both the speed at which something is moving, and on the direction in which it is moving.

A force is needed to cause any acceleration. For motion in a circle, this force is called the **centripetal force** and it always acts towards the centre of the circle. In the case of the motorbike, the centripetal force is provided by friction between its tyres and the road surface. The motorcycle is continuously accelerating towards the centre of the circle.

direction changing

centri for

A The centripetal force is provided by friction between the tyres and the road.

B The centripetal force is provided by forces from the wings.

C A fairground ride.

134

  Turn off   Go Interactive   Pag

Target sheets
Click on this tab to see a target sheet for each unit. Save the target sheet on your computer and you can fill it in on screen. At the end of the topic you can go back and see how much you have learnt by updating the sheet.

sheets ? Help

Help
Click on this tab at any time to search for help on how to use the ActiveBook.

1 What is centripetal force?

2 Look at photo B. The aircraft are travelling at a constant speed. Are they accelerating? Explain your answer.

3 Look at photo C. What is providing the centripetal force?

Force, mass and acceleration are related to each other by the formula force = mass × acceleration. The force needed to produce circular motion therefore depends on both the mass and the acceleration.

The stone has changed direction by this angle in one second.

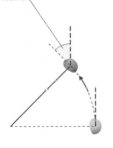

If the stone is swung faster, it changes direction by a bigger angle each second. This greater acceleration requires a bigger centripetal force.

If the string is shorter, the stone changes direction by a bigger angle each second. This greater acceleration requires a bigger centripetal force.

D A higher speed and a smaller circle both need a bigger centripetal force.

The amount of centripetal force needed to keep an object moving in a circle therefore depends on:
- the mass of the object – the greater the mass, the larger the force needed
- the speed at which it is travelling – the higher the speed, the larger the force needed
- the radius of the circle – the smaller the circle, the larger the force needed.

4 Look at photo C. How would the centripetal force be changed if:
  a the ride went faster?
  b the ride went round a shallower curve?
  c there were all adults in the seats instead of children?

5 A lorry and a car are both going around a bend at the same speed. Which one has the greater centripetal force acting on it? Explain your answer.

6 a How do mass, speed and radius affect the size of the centripetal force needed to keep something moving in a circle?
  b Give three examples of circular motion which have different kinds of centripetal force.

135

Zoom feature
Just click on a section of the page and it will magnify so that you can read it easily on screen. This also means that you can look closely at photos and diagrams.

of.256

Page number
You can turn one page at a time, or you can type in the number of the page you want and go straight to that page.

Contents

Exchange and balance

You are continually exchanging substances between the cells of your body and your environment. Some parts of your body – such as your lungs, small intestine and kidneys – have particular adaptations that make them effective as exchange surfaces. Other organisms also have surfaces that are adapted for exchange. For example, fish have gills, and plants have leaves and root hair cells.

When you exercise, the exchange of gases in your lungs and the exchange of gases and dissolved food between your blood and cells become very important in keeping you active. The fitter you are, the better your heart and circulation are able to cope with increased activity. Even if you are very fit there comes a point where muscle cells need even more energy and they need to use anaerobic respiration.

A Keeping fit.

1 Draw a table with these headings. Complete your table to show what you know about substances that are exchanged between your body and your environment.

Substance	Where this is exchanged in the body	Which process in the body this substance is used in

2 Identify any exchanges where you need to find out more.

By the end of this unit you should be able to:

- explain how exchange surfaces in animals and plants are adapted for effective exchange
- describe how blood circulates through the heart and the rest of the body
- explain how the body responds to different levels of exercise
- explain how muscle cells use anaerobic respiration when aerobic respiration cannot supply enough energy for activity
- evaluate different methods for treating kidney failure.

Diffusion and active transport

By the end of this topic you should be able to:

- recall that dissolved substances move by diffusion transport
- explain how active transport moves substances against a concentration gradient using energy.

Photograph A shows what has happened to a thin layer of blue dye that was placed in the middle of some clear agar. The dye particles are able to move through the agar.

1 a Describe what has happened in the tube in photograph A as fully as you can.
  b Suggest what the tube might look like a few hours later.

When particles are free to move, they move randomly and spread throughout an area. We say that the particles are diffusing. Gas particles will diffuse through another gas, or through a liquid. Soluble substances will also diffuse in a liquid or a semi-solid substance like agar.

2 a Draw a series of three diagrams to show:
  (i) a drop of food colouring being placed in a beaker of water
  (ii) the food colouring starting to diffuse through the water
  (iii) what the solution looks like when diffusion is complete.
  b On your second diagram, draw the path of movement of one dye particle since it was placed in the beaker.

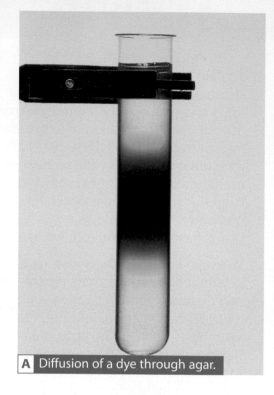

A Diffusion of a dye through agar.

The more particles there are in one place, the more there are to move. So the rate of **diffusion** will be greater.

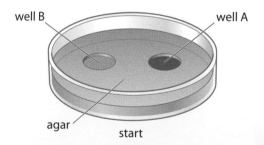

well B   well A

agar
start   one day later

B Different concentrations of dye were placed in each well in the agar and left for 24 hours.

3 Look at diagram B.
  a Explain why the distance the colour has moved in the agar is the same from both wells.
  b Explain why the colour around well A is darker than around well B.
  c Define 'rate of diffusion'.

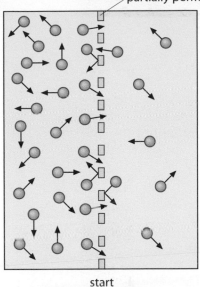
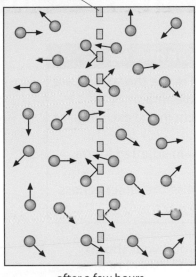

partially permeable membrane

start

after a few hours

C Diffusion across a partially permeable membrane.

Diffusion can also happen across a **partially permeable membrane**, such as a cell membrane. As our bodies contain a high proportion of water, diffusion is an important process for moving soluble substances into and out of cells. The rate of diffusion will depend on the difference in concentration on each side of the membrane. We call this the **concentration gradient**.

H Cells can't depend on diffusion for transporting in and out all the substances they need. Sometimes cells need to transport substances against their concentration gradient. To do this they need to use energy from respiration. This is called **active transport**. The energy is used to move the particles through special channels in the membrane.

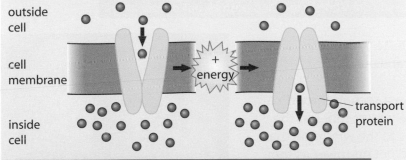

outside cell

cell membrane

inside cell

+ energy

transport protein

D Energy is needed to change the shape of the protein channel.

5 a Explain what is meant by 'against their concentration gradient'.
  b Why can't this movement be done by diffusion?

H 6 a Which organelles in a cell carry out the reactions of respiration?
  b Suggest how you would identify a cell that carries out a lot of active transport.

4 Look at diagram C.
  a Explain the term 'partially permeable membrane'.
  b Describe what is happening to the particles on each side of the membrane.
  c Explain how this leads to the concentration gradient changing across the membrane.

7 a Write a dictionary definition for the word 'diffusion'.
  b Write a dictionary definition for the term 'active transport'.

11

Gas exchange in the lungs

By the end of this topic you should be able to:

- describe how the lungs are protected in the thorax, and are separated from the abdomen by the diaphragm
- explain the role of the breathing system in the exchange of gases between the air and the blood
- describe how the alveoli in the lungs are adapted for gas exchange
- explain how these adaptations maximise the effectiveness of the lungs.

Your lungs are in the upper part of your body, your **thorax**, protected by the ribcage. Below the lungs is a sheet of fibre and muscle called the **diaphragm** that separates the thorax from the **abdomen** below. Movements of the ribcage and diaphragm cause you to breathe in and out.

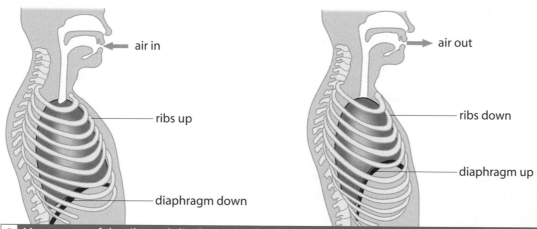

air in

ribs up

diaphragm down

air out

ribs down

diaphragm up

A Movements of the ribs and diaphragm make you draw breath into and push air out of your lungs.

1 Describe as fully as you can what happens to your ribcage and diaphragm when you breathe deeply in and out.

If you cut through a lung it would look like a section through a sponge. It is full of a network of tubes. The widest tubes at the top are called **bronchi**; they link the lungs to the windpipe that goes to your throat. The tubes branch and get narrower as they go deeper into the lungs. Eventually each tube ends in a tiny air sac called an **alveolus**. It is in your alveoli that oxygen and carbon dioxide gases are exchanged with your blood.

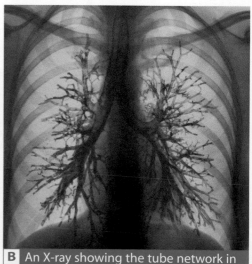

B An X-ray showing the tube network in human lungs.

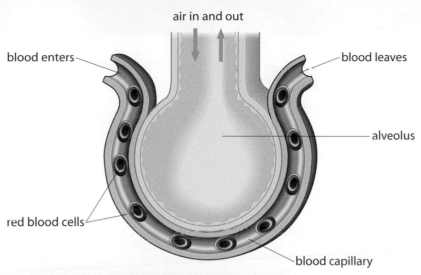

air in and out

blood enters

blood leaves

alveolus

red blood cells

blood capillary

C Each alveolus is very close to a blood **capillary**.

Some estimates suggest that there are over 500 million alveoli in human lungs. These give a surface area for exchange of gases of about 100 m². The larger the surface area for exchange, the more that can be exchanged at the same time. Alveoli and blood capillaries both have very thin walls that are only one cell thick. This means that gases diffusing across them only have a few millimetres to travel and diffusion happens quickly.

Some of the air in your lungs is replaced each time you breathe. This keeps a relatively high concentration of oxygen and a relatively low concentration of carbon dioxide in the lungs. At the same time the blood in the capillaries is continually circulating, bringing blood to the lungs with a high concentration of carbon dioxide and a low concentration of oxygen.

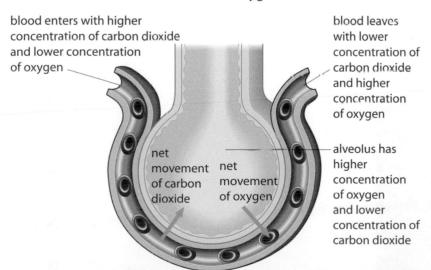

blood enters with higher concentration of carbon dioxide and lower concentration of oxygen

blood leaves with lower concentration of carbon dioxide and higher concentration of oxygen

net movement of carbon dioxide   net movement of oxygen

alveolus has higher concentration of oxygen and lower concentration of carbon dioxide

D Oxygen and carbon dioxide diffuse along their concentration gradients.

The breathing system is usually so effective that all movement of gases between lungs and blood is by diffusion.

2 Describe the path of a molecule of oxygen from the air to a blood capillary in the lungs.

3 Explain the effect of having millions of capillaries in the lungs.

4 Draw a sketch to show why an increased surface area increases the rate of exchange.

5 Explain why a short distance means that diffusion can happen more quickly.

6 a Describe how steep concentration gradients for oxygen and carbon dioxide are maintained in the lungs.
  b Explain why this is important for effective gas exchange in the lungs.

7 Draw a table with these headings. Complete it to show the adaptations of the lungs for gas exchange.

Adaptation of lung	Effect on gas exchange

Absorbing food

By the end of this topic you should be able to:

- describe how the surface of the small intestine is increased by villi
- describe other adaptations of the small intestine for absorption by diffusion, including the extensive network of capillaries
- explain how the adaptations of the small intestine maximise its effectiveness for absorption
- **H** understand that some products of digestion are absorbed by active transport.

When you eat, your food passes through your gut and is **digested** into smaller molecules. Much of the digestion takes place in the stomach and small intestine. You absorb the molecules that you need from the digested food as they pass through your small intestine.

Your small intestine has several features that help you to get the most out of your food. The inner surface of the intestine is covered in small projections called **villi**. These greatly increase the surface area for absorption. By the time the food passes through the small intestine it has the consistency of a mushy soup. Muscles in the wall of the small intestine help make the villi sway to and fro through the 'soup' and bring them into contact with as much of it as possible.

Many of the cells that line the villi have tiny projections of the cell membrane called **microvilli**. These cells form a surface that is just one cell thick that is close to a network of capillaries inside each villus. Each capillary also has a wall that is only one cell thick so that the distance the absorbed substances have to travel to get into the blood is kept to a minimum.

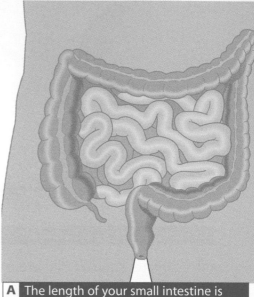

A The length of your small intestine is about three times your height.

1 Explain why the small intestine is so long.

2 How does an increased surface area help absorption?

3 How does moving the villi help improve absorption?

B Villi increase the total surface area of your small intestine to about half the area of a football pitch.

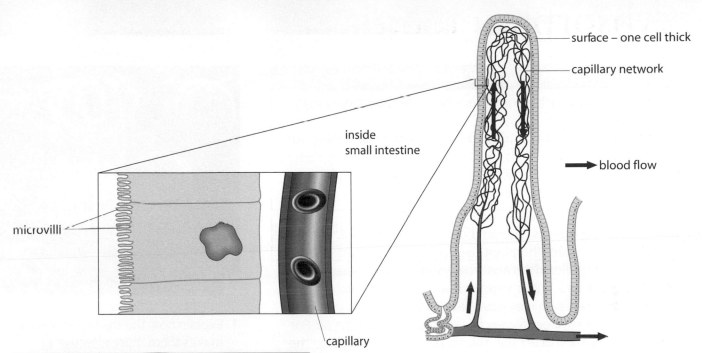

surface – one cell thick

capillary network

blood flow

inside small intestine

microvilli

capillary

C Section through one villus in the small intestine.

4 a What effect do microvilli have on the surface area of the intestine?

b Why is this important?

5 Why does the distance between the inside of the gut and the blood in the capillary network need to be as short as possible?

6 The constantly circulating blood in the capillaries maintains as steep a concentration gradient as possible for the substances being absorbed from the gut.

a Explain what this means.

b Explain why it is important.

Many of the small molecules in the digested food cross from the gut into the blood by diffusion. These include the molecules that make up fats – glycerol and fatty acids – as well as water and mineral ions.

H Other substances, such as glucose and amino acids, may be absorbed from the gut by active transport. This gives the body good control over how much and which of these substances are taken into the blood.

7 a Which large molecules are glucose and amino acids the building blocks for?

b Why does active transport give greater control over how much of a substance is absorbed?

c Explain why there are many mitochondria in cells lining the small intestine.

8 a Draw a concept map that shows all the adaptations of the small intestine for absorption.

b Add to your map explanations of why these adaptations help to maximise the uptake of digested food molecules.

Absorption in plants

By the end of this topic you should be able to:

- describe how carbon dioxide enters a leaf by diffusion through stomata
- describe how water and mineral ions enter plants through root hair cells
- explain how leaves and roots are adapted as exchange surfaces.

During photosynthesis carbon dioxide and water react to make glucose and oxygen. The plant uses energy from light to do this. The carbon dioxide is absorbed and oxygen released through the leaves. Water vapour is another gas which is lost through the leaves. Leaves have several adaptations that make them effective surfaces for exchanging gases with the air. For example they are usually flat, thin and held at an angle to the Sun that captures most light.

Gases diffuse into and out of leaves through **stomata** – tiny holes in the leaf's surface. Generally there are more stomata on the lower surface of a leaf, where they are sheltered from blockage by water and dirt.

Inside the leaf, connected to the stomata, there are many air spaces. This is the surface where the gases are exchanged between the leaf cells and the air.

A Stomata on the underside of a leaf.

1 Explain how the thickness of leaves makes them more effective at exchanging gases.

2 a Name **three** gases that pass through the stomata.
  b In which direction does each of these gases usually move? Explain your answers.

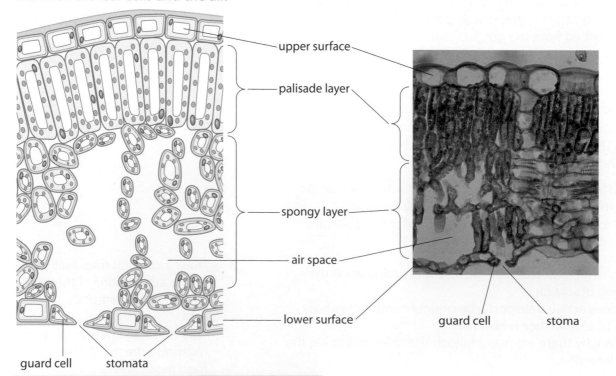

upper surface

palisade layer

spongy layer

air space

lower surface

guard cell   stomata

guard cell   stoma

B The stomata are connected to air spaces in the leaf.

3 Effective exchange surfaces have a large surface area. Explain how this is achieved in a leaf.

4 Look at diagram B.
   a Write down the path that a carbon dioxide molecule takes from the air to a chloroplast in a palisade cell.
   b What is the minimum number of cells that the carbon dioxide has to pass through from the air on the way to a chloroplast?
   c Explain the importance of keeping this number to a minimum.

5 Carbon dioxide moves by diffusion. Which has the greater concentration of carbon dioxide during the day, the air or the cell containing the chloroplast? Explain your answer.

At the other end of the plant, the roots provide the surface where most of the water and dissolved mineral ions are absorbed into the plant. Each root is covered in **root hair cells** which have fine extensions that spread out into the soil.

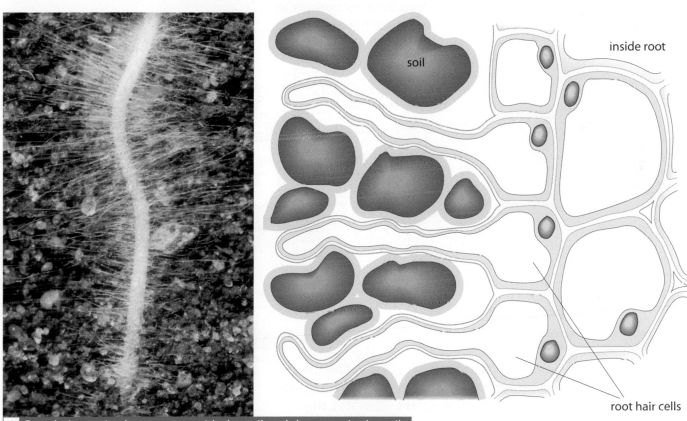

C Root hairs are in close contact with the soil and the water in the soil.

6 a Explain what effect root hair cells have on the surface area for absorption.
   b Why is this important for the plant?

H 7 Dissolved ions in soil water are at a lower concentration than the ions in the cell cytoplasm. Suggest what method a plant uses to absorb mineral ions. Explain your answer.

8 Draw sketches of a leaf and a root. Annotate your sketches to show how they are adapted to make them effective in the exchange of materials.

Movement of water through plants

By the end of this topic you should be able to:

- describe how plants lose water from their leaves by transpiration
- suggest conditions that affect the rate of transpiration
- explain how and why a plant controls the rate of transpiration in some conditions.

Osmosis is the movement of water across a partially permeable membrane from a dilute solution to a more concentrated solution. The concentration of soil water solution is more dilute than the concentration of the cytoplasm in root hair cells, so water moves into those cells by osmosis. This makes their cytoplasm more dilute than the cytoplasm of the cells further inside the root, so water moves from the root hair cells into them by osmosis. In this way water travels across the root until it reaches the **xylem**.

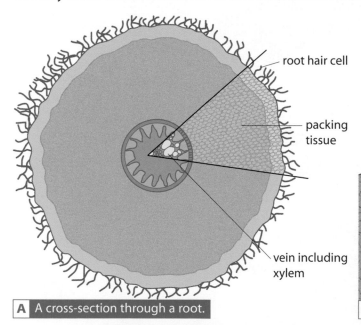

root hair cell

packing tissue

vein including xylem

A A cross-section through a root.

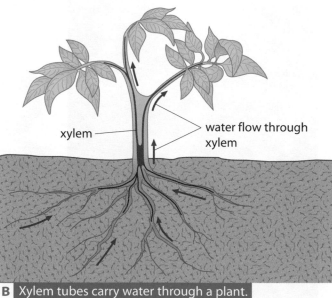

xylem

water flow through xylem

B Xylem tubes carry water through a plant.

In the leaves, water evaporates from the cells that line the air spaces. The water vapour then diffuses out of the leaf through the stomata and into the air. As the water evaporates, this increases the concentration of the cytoplasm in those cells. So water moves by osmosis from the cells that are next to them. This happens from cell to cell across the leaf until the xylem in the leaf vein is reached. There water moves by osmosis from the vein into the cells that surround it.

1 Sketch diagram A. Annotate your sketch to describe how water moves from the soil to the xylem in the centre of the root.

2 Explain how water gets from the roots to the leaves in a plant.

3 Sketch diagram B on page 16. Then annotate your sketch to describe how water moves from the vein through the leaf and evaporates out into the air.

Some of the water that enters a plant through the roots is used for photosynthesis, and some remains inside the plant's cells. About 99% is lost from the plant's surface, mostly through the stomata. This loss of water vapour is called **transpiration**. Transpiration happens more quickly in hot, dry and windy conditions. We can measure the rate of transpiration from a plant in different conditions using a **potometer**.

4 Write a brief plan to investigate the effect of temperature on the rate of transpiration.

5 Suggest why windy conditions increase the rate of transpiration.

If transpiration from the leaves is faster than the rate of osmosis of water into the roots, the plant will start to **wilt**. This happens because water is being taken from the cells and so they become less rigid. If the plant loses too much water from its cells, this affects reactions that take place in the cell and may cause permanent damage. To prevent too much water being lost, **guard cells** can close the stomata in the leaves.

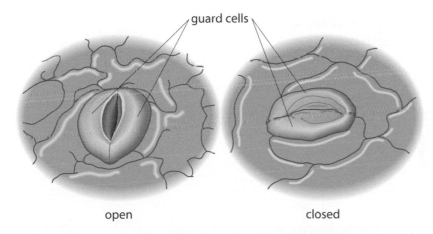

guard cells

open   closed

C The guard cells on each side of a stoma control whether it is open or closed.

6 Suggest conditions that would cause a plant to close its stomata.

7 What effect would this have on the rate of photosynthesis? Explain your answer.

8 Write an entry for an online encyclopaedia to explain transpiration. Your entry should include what it is, why it happens, the problems it may cause a plant, and how the plant controls it.

Human blood circulation

By the end of this topic you should be able to:

- describe how the heart pumps blood through the arteries to the organs, and then through veins back to the heart
- identify two separate circulation systems in humans
- explain how substances are exchanged between body cells and the blood in capillaries.

Your heart is continually beating to pump blood around your body. It pumps blood out through **arteries**. The arteries branch again and again to give narrower vessels that spread throughout the body. Within the organs, the blood vessels are only the width of a red blood cell. These vessels are called **capillaries**.

As they leave the organs, the capillaries join together again and again to form wider vessels called **veins**. By the time they reach the heart all the veins have joined up to form only two large blood vessels.

Diagram A shows a generalised plan of the circulation of blood in humans and other mammals. It shows that for each circulation through the body, the blood passes through the heart twice.

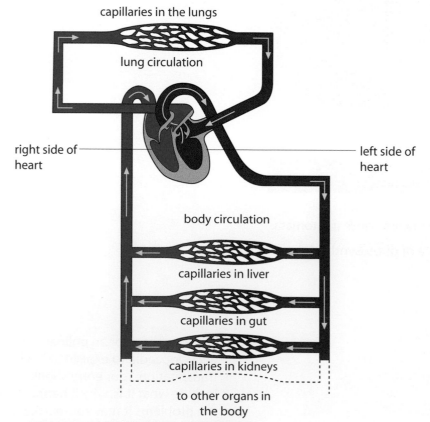

capillaries in the lungs

lung circulation

right side of heart

left side of heart

body circulation

capillaries in liver

capillaries in gut

capillaries in kidneys

to other organs in the body

A Plan of the blood circulation in humans.

1 Look at diagram A. Suggest why it would be difficult to draw a realistic diagram of the human circulation.

2 Give definitions for each of the following: arteries, capillaries, veins.

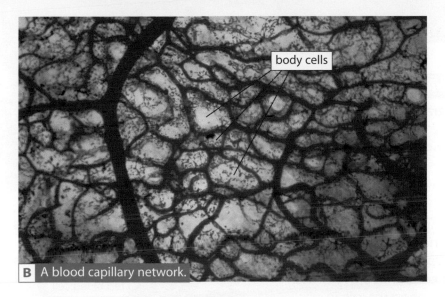

B A blood capillary network.

3 Look at diagram A. Start in the right side of the heart and describe the path of blood movement all the way round back to the right side of the heart again.

4 Describe some changes that happen in the blood as it passes through:
   a capillaries in the body
   b capillaries in the lungs.

The walls of the capillaries are very thin because they are only one cell thick. The capillaries are in close contact with almost every cell in your body. This makes it easy for cells to absorb from the blood the substances that they need to work properly. It is also easy for substances that are made by cells, including hormones such as insulin and waste substances, to pass into the blood for transport to other parts of the body.

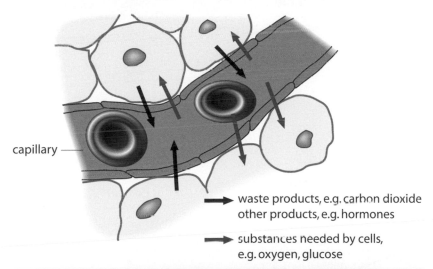

waste products, e.g. carbon dioxide
other products, e.g. hormones

substances needed by cells,
e.g. oxygen, glucose

C Substances are exchanged between the capillaries and cells in the body.

5 Describe the adaptations of capillaries that make them good exchange surfaces with cells.

6 Explain why cells mostly exchange substances with blood in capillaries, rather than in arteries or veins.

7 Blood that has passed through capillaries in the pancreas, picking up insulin, first travels back to the heart rather than directly to cells in the liver and muscles where the insulin is needed. Suggest why this happens.

8 Plan an essay to explain how your blood circulation is effective in supplying all the needs of your cells. Include notes to cover the structure of the circulation, the structure of capillaries, and how these structures contribute to the effectiveness of your circulation.

Travelling in the blood

By the end of this topic you should be able to:

- identify some substances that are transported in blood plasma
- describe red blood cells as having no nucleus and being full of haemoglobin
- explain how oxygen is carried by haemoglobin in red blood cells.

Your blood looks like a red liquid, but the liquid part is not red – it is a pale straw-coloured liquid called **plasma**. This carries many cells, including many **red blood cells** (that are red). Both the plasma and red blood cells play an important role in transporting substances around the body.

1 Explain why blood looks red.

2 Which type of cell is most common in the blood?

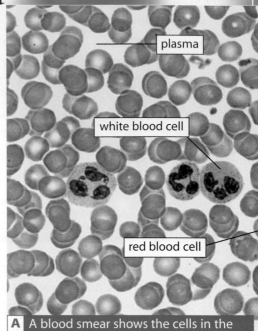

A A blood smear shows the cells in the blood.

plasma

white blood cell

red blood cell

Plasma is mostly water, so soluble substances dissolve easily in it. These substances include carbon dioxide gas and the soluble products of digestion.

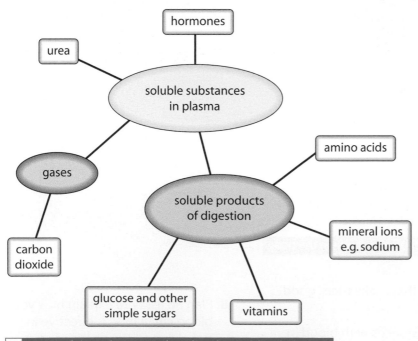

B Some of the substances that dissolve in blood plasma.

hormones

urea

soluble substances in plasma

gases

amino acids

soluble products of digestion

mineral ions e.g. sodium

carbon dioxide

glucose and other simple sugars

vitamins

3 Where in the body do the following diffuse into the plasma:
   a carbon dioxide
   b the soluble products of digestion?

4 Where in the body do the following diffuse out of the plasma:
   a carbon dioxide
   b the soluble products of digestion?

5 Explain why it is possible for urea to be carried around the body in blood plasma.

Urea is another substance that is carried around the body in the blood. It is formed in the liver from the breakdown of amino acids that the body doesn't need. In the kidneys urea is removed from the blood and forms part of urine.

Red blood cells are very unusual cells. They do not contain a nucleus and they have a unique shape. They are packed full of a protein called **haemoglobin**.

Haemoglobin gives red blood cells their red colour. It is also the substance that carries oxygen in the blood. Haemoglobin combines with oxygen to form **oxyhaemoglobin** in the capillaries in the lungs. Oxyhaemoglobin releases the oxygen, to form haemoglobin again, in capillaries in body tissues. The oxygen is then free to diffuse into the body cells.

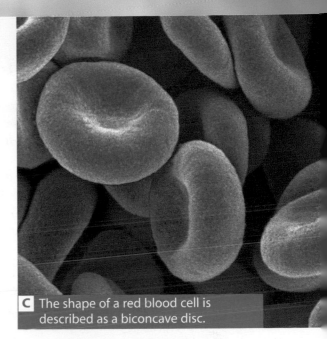

C The shape of a red blood cell is described as a biconcave disc.

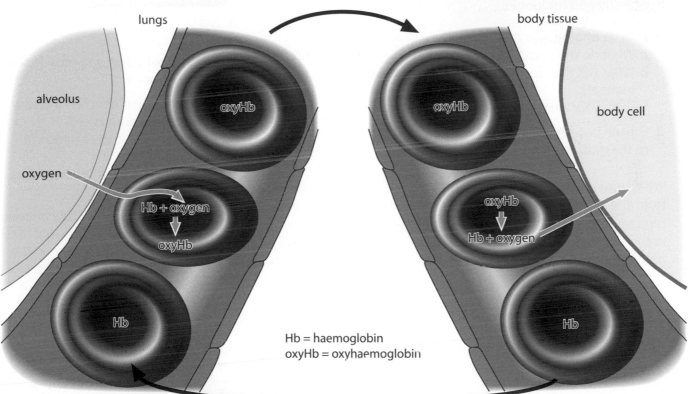

Hb = haemoglobin
oxyHb = oxyhaemoglobin

D Haemoglobin combines reversibly with oxygen.

6 a Suggest what effect the shape of a red blood cell has on the distance for diffusion from the surface to the middle of the cell.
 b Suggest why this is important for its role in carrying oxygen.

7 Describe **two** other adaptations of red blood cells for their role in carrying oxygen.

8 Explain what is meant when we say 'haemoglobin combines reversibly with oxygen'.

9 Complete the following sentence in as many different ways as you can.
The blood carries ... effectively around the body because ...

23

Exercise and the body

By the end of this topic you should be able to:

- explain that some of the energy from respiration is used to make muscles contract
- describe changes that take place in the body during exercise
- interpret data on the effects of exercise on the human body
- explain that the effect of these changes is to supply sugar and oxygen faster to muscles and remove carbon dioxide more rapidly.

A These people are using a lot of energy from respiration.

When your muscles contract they need energy to get shorter. This energy comes from respiration. When you exercise you need more energy so that your muscles can contract more frequently and for longer.

1 Look at photograph A.
   a What do the muscle cells of these people need more of?
   b What will the muscle cells of these people be producing more of?
   Explain your answers.

2 Explain how the substances in your answer to question 1a get to the muscle cells.

When you begin exercising, the amount of oxygen removed from the blood by muscle cells increases. More glucose is also removed from the blood. However, if there isn't enough glucose in the blood for the increased level of respiration, then stores of **glycogen** in muscle and liver cells are converted to glucose to supply what is needed.

3 Explain why liver and muscle cells store glycogen.

4 Describe what effect an increasing level of activity has on:
   a the oxygen concentration in blood near cells
   b the carbon dioxide concentration in blood near cells.

5 The graphs in B show concentrations in venous blood. Explain why these measurements were taken in the veins, not the arteries.

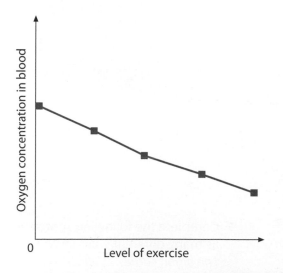
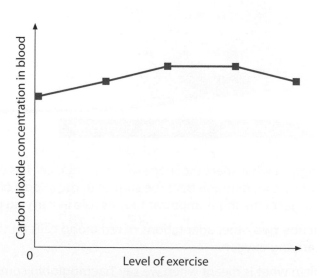

B Concentrations of oxygen and carbon dioxide in the blood change with increasing level of exercise.

To supply all the extra oxygen and sugar that is needed when you exercise, and to remove all the extra carbon dioxide from cells, your blood needs to circulate faster. So your heart beats faster. Oxygen and carbon dioxide also need to be exchanged faster in the lungs, so you breathe faster and more deeply. In addition, the arteries that supply the muscles **dilate** so that they can supply more blood to the muscles more rapidly.

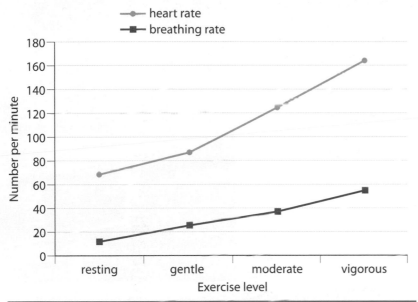

C Heart rate and breathing rate increase with an increasing level of exercise.

If you exercise regularly your body gets fitter and better able to provide the increased blood supply that muscles need during activity. Our bodies are naturally designed for regular and frequent activity. In the UK 7 out of 10 adults don't get enough exercise. This is leading to an increase in health problems, such as high blood pressure and heart disease.

D Many people now go to the gym to get more exercise.

6 The rate of diffusion across a membrane, such as between a blood capillary and the inside of the lung, is affected by the difference in concentration across the membrane. Explain how breathing faster and deeper increases the rate of exchange of oxygen and carbon dioxide between the blood and air in the lungs.

7 Explain why regular activity is important for keeping you healthy.

8 Draw a concept map to show how your body responds to increased exercise. Add notes to your map to explain why those changes happen.

Fatigue and anaerobic respiration

By the end of this topic you should be able to:

- understand that muscles become fatigued after long periods of activity
- explain that anaerobic respiration supplies energy to muscle cells if too little oxygen is available
- **H** • describe how anaerobic respiration produces lactic acid and some energy, and results in an oxygen debt that has to be repaid.

A This athlete's muscles are painful after a long period of vigorous activity.

If you exercise for a long time, your muscles start to **fatigue**. This means that they don't contract as well as they normally do. The cause of this fatigue is uncertain. It used to be thought that it was the result of anaerobic respiration.

Most of the time muscles get the energy they need to contract from **aerobic respiration**, where oxygen from air is used to break down glucose. But if oxygen levels in the muscles are low they can also use **anaerobic respiration**. This doesn't need oxygen to break down glucose, but still releases energy for contraction. Oxygen levels in muscle cells may be too low either when you suddenly start exercising vigorously, or after exercising vigorously for a long time.

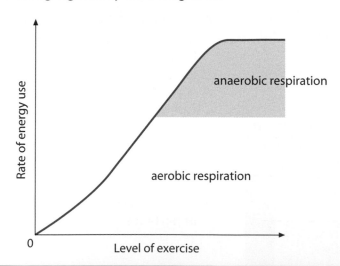

B Graph showing the source of energy at different levels of activity.

1 Explain what we mean by 'muscle fatigue'.

2 a Give **one** similarity between aerobic and anaerobic respiration.
   b Give **one** difference between the two types of respiration.

3 Suggest why the oxygen concentration in muscle cells may be low during vigorous activity.

H Anaerobic respiration breaks down glucose, but it doesn't make the same products as aerobic respiration. The equation for anaerobic respiration is:

glucose $\longrightarrow$ **lactic acid** (+ energy released)

Anaerobic respiration produces much less energy than aerobic respiration for each glucose molecule that is broken down. This is because the glucose is only partly broken down and there is still a lot of energy locked in the bonds of the lactic acid molecules. However, the breakdown of glucose to lactic acid is much faster than the breakdown of glucose to carbon dioxide and water, so anaerobic respiration can supply energy quickly.

4 a Give **one** disadvantage of anaerobic respiration compared with aerobic respiration.
b Give **one** advantage of anaerobic respiration.

Once the exercise level has reduced, we have to get rid of the lactic acid. It is transported in the blood to the liver where some of it is converted back to glucose using oxygen. For a while we continue to breathe fast and deeply after exercise to supply this extra oxygen. This is often described as 'paying back the **oxygen debt**'. It used to be thought that lactic acid caused muscle fatigue, but scientists now realise that it plays an essential part in keeping muscles working when they are being overstimulated.

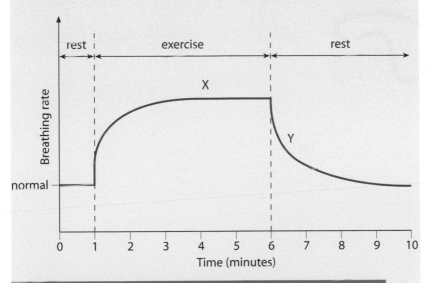

C Breathing rate during and after a period of strenuous exercise.

5 a Explain the breathing rate at point X in graph C.
b Explain the breathing rate at point Y in graph C.

6 a Define 'oxygen debt'.
b Explain what is meant by 'paying back the oxygen debt'.

7 Explain why anaerobic respiration is important in prolonged vigorous exercise.

8 Draw up a table to show the advantages and disadvantages of anaerobic respiration compared with aerobic respiration.

Healthy kidneys

By the end of this topic you should be able to:

- describe how a healthy kidney produces urine by filtering the blood, then reabsorbing sugar and any ions and water that the body needs
- explain that urine contains urea, excess ions and water
- explain that sugar and dissolved ions may be actively absorbed in the kidneys.

You have two kidneys that are about halfway down your back and inside your abdomen. Their role is to filter your blood and remove some of the substances your body doesn't need. Each kidney is made up of over one million **tubules**.

At the start of each tubule is a small capillary network called a **glomerulus**. The cells that line these capillaries have very leaky membranes. This allows a lot of plasma, and the substances dissolved in it, to be filtered from the blood through into the tubule.

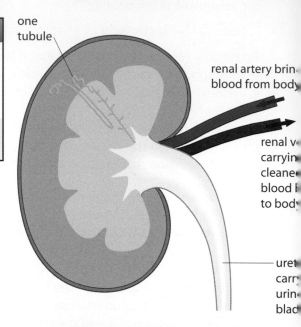

one tubule

renal artery bring blood from body

renal v carryin cleane blood to body

uret carry urin blad

A Section through a kidney showing its blood supply.

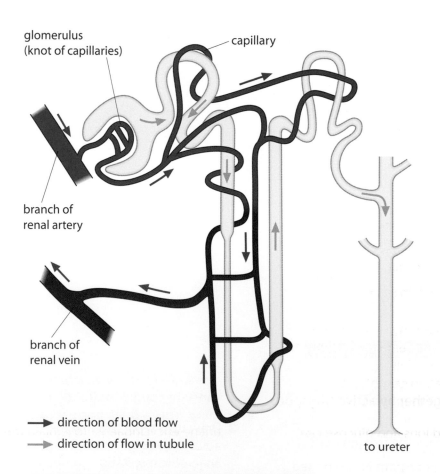

glomerulus (knot of capillaries)

capillary

branch of renal artery

branch of renal vein

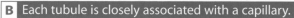

→ direction of blood flow

→ direction of flow in tubule

to ureter

B Each tubule is closely associated with a capillary.

1 Suggest some of the substances dissolved in plasma that could pass into the tubule.

2 Which structures in blood cannot pass into the tubule? Explain your answer.

3 Suggest why each tubule is closely associated with a capillary.

As the fluid passes along the tubule, many of the substances in it are absorbed back into the capillary – all the sugar (glucose) is reabsorbed, for example. This is important because the body uses glucose for respiration. Also any dissolved ions and water that the body needs are reabsorbed. This makes sure that the right balance of water and ions is maintained in the body so that cells and all the processes in them can work properly.

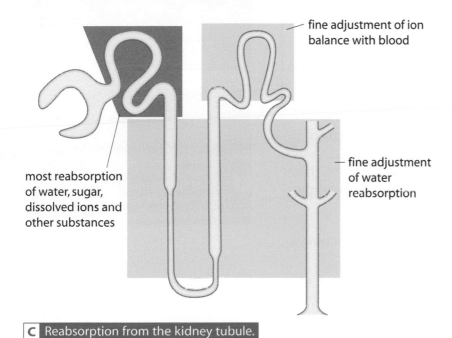

fine adjustment of ion balance with blood

most reabsorption of water, sugar, dissolved ions and other substances

fine adjustment of water reabsorption

C Reabsorption from the kidney tubule.

The fluid that remains in the tubule is called **urine**. It passes into the ureter and then to the bladder for excretion.

4 Doctors sometimes test a patient's urine for glucose. Explain why glucose in the urine indicates that there is a problem.

5 Suggest **one** symptom that a patient would suffer if they were losing glucose in their urine. Explain your answer.

6 If you drink the same amount of liquids, you will produce less urine on a hot day than on a cold day. Explain why.

7 What does urine normally contain? Explain your answer.

H The water that is reabsorbed moves back into the blood by osmosis. Some of the substances that are reabsorbed from the tubule into the blood move by diffusion. This includes some of the dissolved ions and glucose. However, the rest of the glucose and dissolved ions are reabsorbed together by active transport.

8 a Suggest why some of the dissolved ions and glucose can move back into the blood by diffusion.
b Explain why the rest of the glucose and ions that are reabsorbed are moved using active transport.

9 Homeostasis is the maintenance of constant conditions inside the body. Write a brief article for an online encyclopaedia to explain the role of the kidneys in homeostasis. Include headings on structure, filtration and reabsorption.

Dialysis treatment

By the end of this topic you should be able to:

- describe how a person with kidney failure may be treated with dialysis and explain why it has to be carried out at regular intervals
- describe how substances are exchanged between dialysis fluid and the patient's blood across partially permeable membranes to restore normal levels in the blood
- evaluate the advantages and disadvantages of dialysis treatment.

Many people have kidney disease, sometimes without even knowing it. Many things can cause it, such as infection, diabetes, long-term high blood pressure or damage in an accident. The treatment offered by a doctor will depend on the cause of the disease.

1 Suggest why people can have kidney disease without knowing it.

2 Explain why a stone blocking the ureter could affect how a kidney works.

Only a small proportion of people with kidney disease will eventually develop **kidney failure**. This is defined as occurring when less than 30% of the kidneys function properly. At this stage the body can be affected badly by the lack of kidney function.

3 a Explain as fully as you can what will happen to the concentration of substances in the blood if the kidneys are failing.
  b Suggest what effect this will have on the cells in the body.

One way of treating kidney failure is **haemodialysis**. This is when a machine takes over the function of the kidneys. Needles are inserted into blood vessels, often in the patient's arm. Blood flows from the patient through a tube to the machine and is returned through another tube. Inside the machine the blood flows through a filter called a **dialyser**.

Inside the dialyser, a partially permeable membrane separates the blood from the dialysing fluid. This fluid contains the right proportions of substances to allow diffusion of waste products, such as urea and excess substances, out of the blood. It also ensures that glucose and useful mineral ions aren't lost from the blood during dialysis.

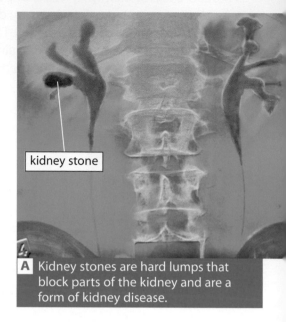

kidney stone

A Kidney stones are hard lumps that block parts of the kidney and are a form of kidney disease.

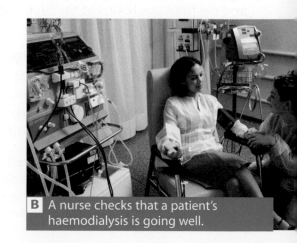

B A nurse checks that a patient's haemodialysis is going well.

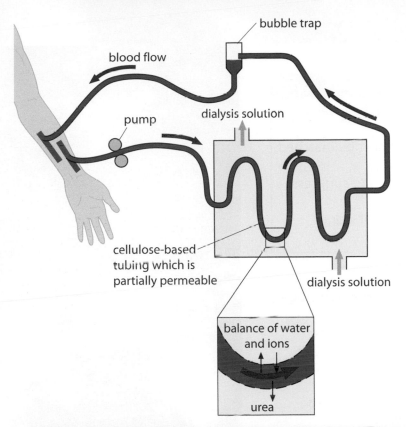

bubble trap

blood flow

pump

dialysis solution

cellulose-based tubing which is partially permeable

dialysis solution

balance of water and ions

urea

C Diffusion into and out of the blood happens in a dialyser just like in the kidney.

4 a Explain how the dialyser mimics the normal function of the kidney.

H **b** In what way does the dialyser *not* mimic the normal function of the kidney?

D Peritoneal dialysis uses a natural membrane in the abdomen as the dialysis membrane.

How good is dialysis?

Dialysis only partly copies the action of the kidney. So people with kidney failure also need to control their diet to prevent a build-up of particular substances, and to avoid taking in too much fluid. Peritoneal dialysis is done continually and you can move around at the same time, but the patient and family have to be careful to carry out the dialysis properly. Haemodialysis is usually done three times a week, for about four hours each time, and often in hospital with supervision. Without treatment, a patient with kidney failure would eventually fall into a coma and die from the toxins in the blood or from a heart attack.

5 Describe **one** advantage of using dialysis to treat kidney failure.

6 Make a list of the disadvantages of using dialysis for treating kidney failure.

7 Write a brief article for a website that explains to kidney disease patients how dialysis is used to treat these patients.

Kidney transplants

By the end of this topic you should be able to:

- explain that a person with kidney failure can be given a healthy kidney in a transplant
- explain why the tissue of the new kidney must be matched with the patient
- explain why the patient is treated with drugs to suppress the immune system
- evaluate the advantages and disadvantages of kidney transplants.

Another way of treating kidney failure is to give the patient a healthy kidney. This is called a **transplant**. The patient must be as healthy as possible before the operation because the transplant operation puts the body under strain. Only one kidney is transplanted, because your body can manage with just one good kidney.

1 a Explain why a patient with kidney failure who also has a heart problem may not be given a transplant.
b What other option is there for treatment of this kind of patient?

A major problem with the transplant of any organ is the risk of **rejection** of the transplanted tissue. The cells in your body have markers on the outside which show that they are *your* cells. The types of markers depend on your genes. Your immune system will attack anything that has different markers, such as invading pathogens or cells from another person's body.

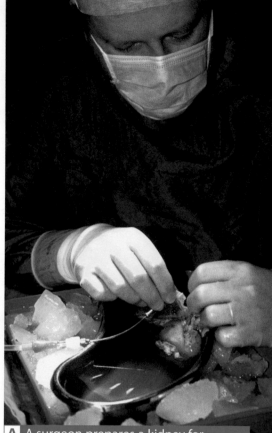

A A surgeon prepares a kidney for transplant.

2 a Explain why the cell marker system is useful for protecting your body against many kinds of infection.
b Explain why it is a problem in transplants.

3 Explain why the markers on your cells will be more like those on your mother's cells than those of someone who isn't related to you.

In the UK, in about one-third of transplants the kidney is donated by a living relative or friend. Otherwise kidneys for transplant come from people who have died in accidents or from a stroke. Patients waiting for kidney transplants are put on a national register. When a kidney becomes available, the **tissue type** and blood type of the dead or dying person are compared with those on the register and the kidney is offered to the patient with the best match.

kidney for transplant

tissue type

A, B and DR are three key cell markers. There are at least 20 versions of each marker.

patient A
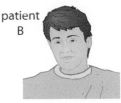
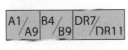

patient B
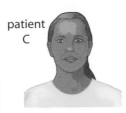
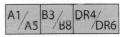

patient C
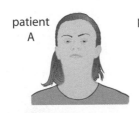
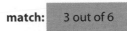

match: 3 out of 6   4 out of 6   6 out of 6   best match

B Making the best match.

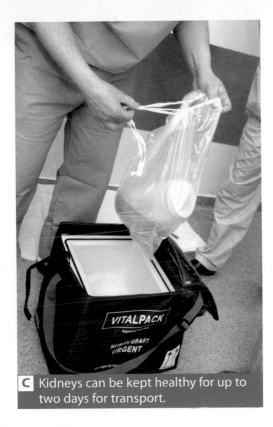

C Kidneys can be kept healthy for up to two days for transport.

4 Explain why a kidney from a person who died in Scotland can be used for a patient in Cornwall.

5 Why is the kidney offered to the person with the best match?

6 Explain why a relative can offer one of their kidneys to a transplant patient.

No matter how good the tissue match is, after the operation the patient will have to take **immunosuppressant drugs** for the rest of his or her life – these stop the immune system attacking the new kidney.

Problems with transplants

A transplanted kidney may be rejected immediately or slowly over many years. On average a transplanted kidney lasts about eight years. During this time the patient is able to lead a more normal life than someone on dialysis. However, the drugs they take increase their risks of catching other infections, and also the chances of getting some kinds of cancer.

7 Draw up a table to show the advantages and disadvantages of kidney transplants.

8 Design a poster for a hospital waiting room to explain how patients are chosen for kidney transplants, and why it is best to wait for the right one.

These questions are about Leanne's investigation into the effect of wind speed on the rate of transpiration. You should use the results below, as well as your understanding of how these investigations are carried out, to answer the questions.

Leanne used a potometer, as shown in the diagram, to measure the rate of transpiration. The fan had three speed settings that produced different wind speeds across the plant shoot.

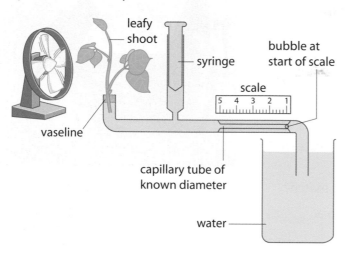

Leanne set the fan to speed 0 – so the plant got only the air movement in the room – and left the equipment for five minutes. She then adjusted the bubble in the potometer to zero and took readings every minute for five minutes. Leanne repeated this method for speed settings 1, 2 and 3 which got increasingly windy. The table shows her results.

Speed setting	Time (minutes)					
	0	1	2	3	4	5
0	0	0.7	1.2	1.8	2.4	3.0
1	0	0.7	1.3	2.0	2.2	3.5
2	0	0.9	1.7	2.7	3.7	4.6
3	0	0.1	0.1	0.2	0.3	0.3

1 What kind of variable is the speed setting of the fan:
   • a control variable
   • a discrete variable
   • an ordered variable
   • a dependent variable? *(1 mark)*

2 What equipment could Leanne have used to measure wind speed as a continuous variable? *(1 mark)*

3 Explain why Leanne left the equipment for five minutes at each new setting before starting the measurements. *(1 mark)*

4 Has Leanne carried out a fair test? Explain your answer. *(2 marks)*

5 A simpler investigation would have been to measure the weight of a plant in a pot before and after putting it in front of the fan for five minutes. Explain why Leanne's method produces better results. *(1 mark)*

6 Draw a circle around any anomalous results in Leanne's table. *(1 mark)*

7 Explain how Leanne can use her results to calculate the rate of transpiration for speed 2. *(1 mark)*

8 Leanne is trying to decide how best to present her results. Which of the following would be the best graph to draw:
   • bar chart
   • line graph
   • pie chart
   • scatter graph? *(1 mark)*

9 Explain how Leanne could improve the validity of her results. *(1 mark)*

10 Describe **one** way that Leanne could increase the accuracy of her results. *(1 mark)*

11 ✎ Describe *fully* the relationship between rate of transpiration and wind speed shown by Leanne's results. Then write a conclusion based on the evidence from this investigation. *(4 marks)*

Exploiting microorganisms

A What impact does biotechnology have on your life?

Even thousands of years ago, people from countries as far apart as Egypt, Japan and Peru knew how to use microorganisms in their local communities to make useful products like bread, beer and wine. Today these products are manufactured on an industrial scale using similar microorganisms.

The modern biotechnology industry is just over thirty years old and produces medicines such as penicillin, and foods such as **mycoprotein**. These products are made in large **bioreactors** or **fermenters**. Growth of the microorganisms occurs at moderate temperatures, and the nutrients needed can be supplied from the waste products of other processes. They generate little waste as they grow.

All the raw materials and equipment must be sterilised before production begins so that only the desired microorganisms are grown. This is to avoid disease and contamination of the end product.

1 **a** Make a list of as many products as you can think of that are made using microorganisms.
  b Next to each of the items in your list state how confident you are of your answer. Use red, amber, green to show this – use red for not very confident, and green for very confident.

> **By the end of this unit you should be able to:**
> - explain how we can use microorganisms safely
> - outline the development of the theory of biogenesis
> - explain how microorganisms are used to make food and drink
> - describe the operation of industrial fermenters in the growth of the fungi *Penicillium* and *Fusarium*
> - Explain how fuels such as biogas and ethanol can be produced by anaerobic fermentation.

Growing microorganisms

By the end of this topic you should be able to:

- describe how microorganisms are grown in a culture medium
- describe the conditions that microorganisms need in order to reproduce
- explain why the incubation temperature is lower in a school laboratory than in industry.

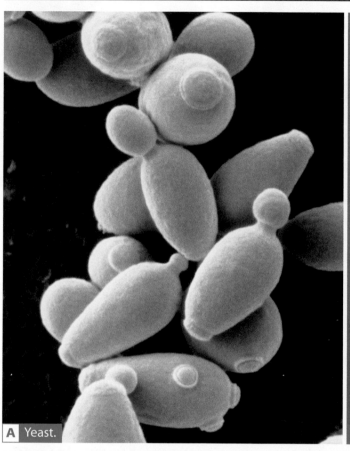

A Yeast.

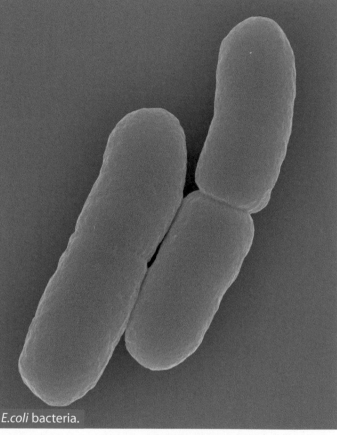

E.coli bacteria.

Like all living organisms, bacteria and fungi need nutrients to grow and reproduce. They use carbohydrates such as starch and glucose for the energy that they need. They also need a source of nitrogen, such as mineral ions or urea, so that they can synthesise their own proteins. Other mineral ions, such as potassium and phosphorus, are also needed sometimes. To ensure that the microbes reach their optimal growth rate, additional protein and vitamins may also be supplied.

In the laboratory, nutrients are often supplied to the microbes in a jelly called **agar**. Agar is called a growth or **culture medium**. It melts at 98°C and, as a liquid, it can be poured into plastic or glass Petri dishes. It solidifies at about 44°C. Microbes cannot digest agar so it is not used up as they grow.

1 What nutrients supply microbes with:
   a energy
   b nitrogen?

2 Suggest why agar is called a 'growth medium'.

3 Describe what a Petri dish is and what it is used for.

Besides nutrients, many microbes need a temperature between 25°C and 45°C to grow. In school laboratories the Petri dishes are put into a cabinet or incubator set at a maximum temperature of 25°C. Pathogens could accidentally be present in the culture dishes, so keeping the temperature at the lower end of the range minimises health risks from them.

Conditions in industry

In industry the culture vessels may be kept at temperatures over 30°C. These temperatures cause a higher rate of growth and a higher yield of useful products made by the microbes. Contamination in industry is prevented by the stringent sterile procedures used.

4 What is the maximum temperature used to incubate bacteria in school laboratories? Explain your answer.

5 Explain why higher incubation temperatures are used in industry.

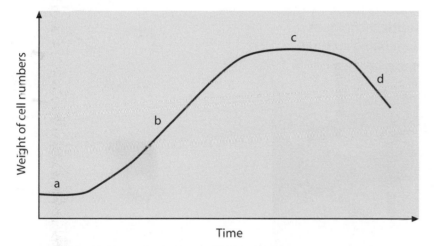

B Bacteria grow quickly in certain conditions.

As unicellular microorganisms grow, their number increases rapidly. Bacterial cells can double their number every 20 minutes in ideal conditions.

6 a Suggest which region of graph B corresponds to ideal growth conditions.

b Give a reason for your answer.

After two days incubating in a Petri dish, colonies of bacteria appear on the surface of the agar. Each colony consists of millions of bacteria – each colony has grown from one single bacterium.

7 Microorganisms can also be cultured in glass flasks in a liquid growth medium called **broth**.

a Suggest what nutrients are added to the flask to encourage microbial growth.

b (i) Where will the flask be incubated in a school laboratory?

(ii) Why is incubation necessary?

c (i) Suggest an alternative growth medium to broth.

(ii) Describe how the alternative you suggested in part (i) differs from broth.

Aseptic technique

By the end of this topic you should be able to:

- recall that you need uncontaminated cultures of microorganisms to get useful products from microorganisms
- describe how apparatus is sterilised and how this achieves pure cultures
- explain how to inoculate a culture medium.

The air, the surfaces around you, your skin and clothes all have microorganisms on them. If you culture microorganisms in the laboratory, it involves growing very large numbers of bacterial or fungal cells. If safety procedures are not followed you may accidentally introduce a harmful microbe into a harmless **strain** that you are growing. This would multiply rapidly, just as the harmless microbes do, and would be a greater health risk than if it were a single cell. This means that any products made by the bacteria would not be usable. Sterile or **aseptic** techniques must therefore be used to prepare uncontaminated cultures.

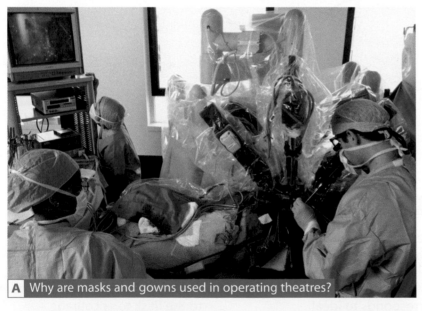

A Why are masks and gowns used in operating theatres?

Glassware and culture media are sterilised in an **autoclave** using pressurised steam at a temperature of 121°C for 15 minutes. The high temperature needed to kill microbes melts plastic and so Petri dishes and disposable instruments are sterilised by ultraviolet or ionising radiation. This is done commercially. Petri dishes remain sterile inside until the lid is opened.

1 What is another name for 'sterile technique'?

2 a Describe what would happen if a single cell of a pathogen entered a culture dish.
 b Explain why this is avoided.

3 Explain how equipment is sterilised if it is made of:
 a glass
 b plastic.

upward draught

Bunsen burner

McCartney bottle

Petri dish lid

sterile agar

Petri dish base

inoculating loop

McCartney bottle

agar slope

① Pour the plate

② Sterilise the inoculating loop in a flame

③ Collect the microbes from the pure culture

upward draught

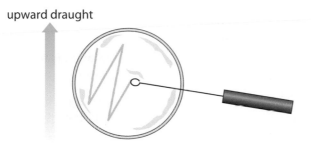

J. Smith   E. coli

3/9/07

④ Inoculate the Petri dish by sweeping the loop back and forth across the agar surface, with the lid held at an angle

⑤ Write the details on the base of the sealed Petri dish

B Preparing to culture microbes.

You must wash your hands before and after working with microorganisms. A clean, cleared working surface is also essential. Hair should be tied back, broken skin covered with a plaster and hand-to-face contact avoided while culturing microbes. Work is carried out near the upward draught from a lighted Bunsen burner to minimise the risk of airborne microbes falling onto culture plates.

Inoculation is the process of transferring microbes to the culture medium. For solid agar, a wire inoculating loop is used. It is first sterilised by holding it in the hottest part of a Bunsen burner flame. After ten seconds cooling, near the Bunsen burner, the microbes can be picked up from the **pure culture** and transferred to the sterile agar by gently sweeping the loop back and forth over the surface.

4 Explain why the wire loop needs to be cooled before picking up the microbes.

5 Suggest why the lid of the Petri dish is not removed completely when introducing the microbes.

Before incubation the Petri dishes are sealed with adhesive tape to prevent contamination from airborne bacteria. After 24 to 72 hours, when the results have been noted, the cultures are autoclaved by a technician before disposal.

6 a Draw a flow diagram to show how you would safely culture the *E. coli* bacterium in the laboratory.
 b Underline in red the safety precautions that you would take at each stage.
 c Explain what would happen to your successful culture after the experiment.
 d What would happen to a sterile Petri dish with agar but no microbes after incubation?

Biogenesis

By the end of this topic you should be able to:

- describe Spallanzani's challenge to the theory of 'spontaneous generation'
- explain Schwann's cell theory
- describe how Pasteur's experiments totally refuted spontaneous generation
- explain what is meant by 'biogenesis'.

Until the eighteenth century people believed that fully formed living organisms could come into existence by **spontaneous generation** or **abiogenesis**. This is the theory that non-living matter can give rise to living organisms. People developed these beliefs from what they saw going on around them. Unlike you, they did not know about the scientific method of investigation and how to use experimental results to arrive at reliable explanations of observations.

In 1776 an Italian priest and scientist called Lazarro Spallanzani made a serious attack on spontaneous generation in a book he wrote. The believers of spontaneous generation thought there was a 'life force' present in the molecules of all inorganic matter, including air. They believed that this could cause spontaneous generation producing microorganisms in chicken broth. Spallanzani knew that boiling microorganisms killed them so he investigated whether or not microorganisms appeared spontaneously after boiling.

1 Explain what is meant by 'abiogenesis'.

2 List the stages in a scientific investigation.

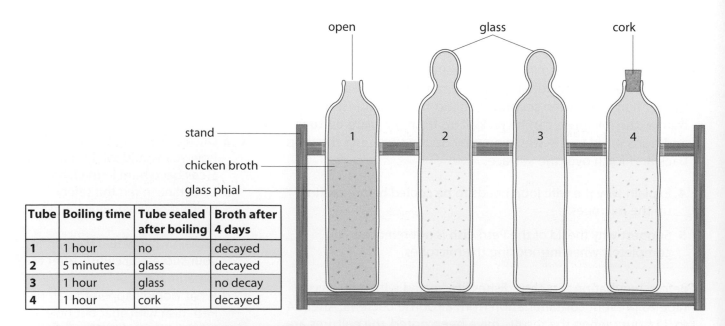

Tube	Boiling time	Tube sealed after boiling	Broth after 4 days
1	1 hour	no	decayed
2	5 minutes	glass	decayed
3	1 hour	glass	no decay
4	1 hour	cork	decayed

A Spallanzani boiled chicken broth in glass tubes, called phials, and waited for four days.

Since no bacteria grew in the tube that was boiled for an hour and then sealed, Spallanzani concluded that spontaneous generation does not occur. His opponents argued that he had only proved that spontaneous generation could not occur without air, and that it is this that contained a 'life force'.

Debate about spontaneous generation carried on for nearly another hundred years. Meanwhile in Berlin a German scientist, Theodor Schwann, was studying cells and tissues. During his research Schwann began to realise that all animal and plant cells contain a nucleus. This led him to propose the **cell theory** which states that:

- all living organisms are composed of one or more cells
- cells are the basic unit of structure and function
- all cells come from pre-existing cells by cell division.

Armed with this knowledge, in 1864 a French chemist called Louis Pasteur set out to disprove spontaneous generation conclusively. He wanted to let air into a broth culture (and therefore if a 'life force' existed it would enter too) but at the same time he wanted to keep bacteria out. He devised a piece of apparatus called the **swan-neck flask** that allowed bacteria to settle out on the wall of the neck as air passed through it.

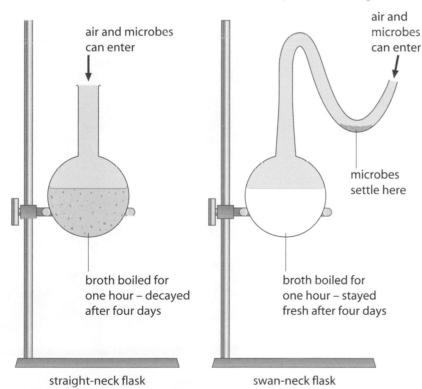

air and microbes can enter

air and microbes can enter

microbes settle here

broth boiled for one hour – decayed after four days

broth boiled for one hour – stayed fresh after four days

straight-neck flask

swan-neck flask

C Pasteur used flasks like these.

Pasteur concluded that there is no 'life force' and organisms do not arise by spontaneous generation. Instead the theory of **biogenesis** was established – this is the process of living organisms producing other living organisms.

3 What is the difference between the treatment of tubes 2 and 3 in diagram A?

Dividing bacterium.

A flower seed develops here.

Human embryo on a pin head.

B Cell theory is one of the foundations of biology.

4 When Pasteur broke the long necks off some of the swan-neck flasks, what do you think happened to the broth inside them? Explain your answer.

5 Pasteur concluded from his experiments that 'all life is from life'. Construct a concept map to show how his work, and that of Spallanzani and Schwann, made this possible.

41

Yoghurt and cheese

By the end of this topic you should be able to:

- recall that bacteria are needed to manufacture yoghurt and cheese
- describe the role of bacteria in yoghurt production
- describe the role of lactic acid in yoghurt manufacture and where it comes from.

Bacterial cells have cytoplasm and a thick cell wall but no nucleus. Many of them feed on organic food which they digest with enzymes they secrete outside the cell.

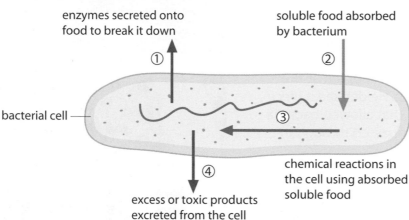

enzymes secreted onto food to break it down ①

soluble food absorbed by bacterium ②

bacterial cell ③

④ chemical reactions in the cell using absorbed soluble food

excess or toxic products excreted from the cell

A The products of bacteria are widely used by humans.

Lactic acid is one of the excreted bacterial products used in the manufacture of yoghurt and cheese. Both manufacturing processes involve the **fermentation** of milk. The cultures of bacteria used are known as **starters**. *Streptococcus thermophilus* and *Lactobacillus bulgaricus* are two species of bacteria that produce lactic acid – they are used in yoghurt production. The milk is incubated at 40–46°C for four to six hours.

3 Explain what is meant by a 'starter culture'.

4 Describe the conditions needed for making yoghurt.

Lactose is the sugar in milk. During the manufacture of yoghurt it is used as a source of chemical energy by the bacteria. They ferment the lactose anaerobically, producing lactic acid as a waste product and releasing chemical energy for use in the cells. The energy is used in the cells for growth, reproduction and chemical synthesis. Lactic acid is excreted from the bacterial cells into the milk. It causes the pH of the milk to fall from 6.3 to 4.6. This lowering of pH causes the protein in milk to turn to a gel and the milk clots partially or solidifies into yoghurt.

1 What chemicals do the bacteria use to digest their food?

2 Explain why bacterial cells can absorb the food substances after digestion.

B Industrial yoghurt production is a highly automated production process.

5 Explain:
   a what lactose is
   b what it supplies to bacterial cells.

6 What process is used by lactic acid-producing bacteria to release energy?

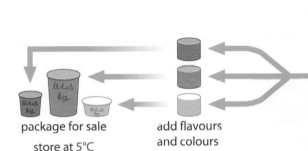

milk powder — thickens the milk

milk is homogenised breaks up fat droplets

pasteurisation kills all bacteria

85–95°C for 15–30 minutes

farm milk

cooled to 40–46°C

starter bacterial culture added

incubation pH falls to 4.6

stir yoghurt and cool to 5°C slows down bacterial activity

package for sale store at 5°C

add flavours and colours

fermenter

kept at 40–46°C for 4–5 hours

C Fermenting milk to produce yoghurt.

You are probably aware of the huge choice of yoghurt available to consumers. For example, it varies in flavour, texture and enrichment with fruit and cereal. *Live* yoghurt contains the living bacteria that were used in its production. *Probiotic* yoghurt has additional bacteria added to it after processing. These bacteria grow in the intestine and can be helpful after suffering from diarrhoea. Bacteria are also used in cheese manufacture.

D Cheese production.

Traditionally, bacteria that produce lactic acid, of the species *Streptococcus cremoris*, and a milk clotting enzyme called **rennin** are used to curdle or sour milk. When milk curdles it separates into solid white particles called **curds** and a watery liquid called **whey**. The curds are pressed into containers to form firm cheeses.

7 a Describe the **two** substances added to milk in the manufacture of cheese.
b Explain what their role in cheese production is.

8 a Explain the difference between 'curds' and 'whey'.
b Which of them makes up the finished cheese?

9 a Copy diagram A and use it to represent a lactic acid-producing bacterium in yoghurt manufacture. Add to it the following words: lactic acid, lactose, respiration.
b Lightly shade where the milk would be and label it.
c Add some small patches of darker shading to show the clots that would form yoghurt and label them.
d Annotate your diagram to show the incubation temperature and the pH change during the conversion of milk to yoghurt.

Yeast

> **By the end of this topic you should be able to:**
>
> - describe the structure of yeast
> - describe how yeast can respire aerobically and anaerobically
> - link the products of yeast's anaerobic respiration to its use in making food and drink.

Yeast is a single-celled fungus. Each cell is oval or spherical and has a nucleus, cytoplasm and a cell membrane surrounded by a cell wall. When a culture of yeast is supplied with glucose, oxygen and water at a temperature of 28°C it will reproduce asexually by **budding**.

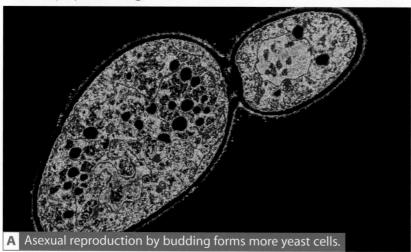

A Asexual reproduction by budding forms more yeast cells.

Some fruits – like grapes, plums and apples – often have a pale grey 'bloom' on their surface. This is partly due to naturally occurring yeast. If you have ever polished a plum or apple by rubbing it on your clothes, you have removed the natural yeast! Yeast also occurs on plant leaves, flowers and in the soil.

All living organisms must release energy by respiration to use in their body processes. The single cell body of yeast can respire in two ways – aerobically and anaerobically.

Aerobic respiration happens when oxygen is available. This produces carbon dioxide and water:

  sugar + oxygen ⟶ carbon dioxide + water + energy

Anaerobic respiration happens when oxygen is unavailable. This produces carbon dioxide and ethanol (alcohol):

  sugar ⟶ ethanol + carbon dioxide + energy

During anaerobic respiration, or fermentation, some of the energy in sugars is not fully released. This means that the energy yield in the cells is much less than in aerobic respiration. It is not enough for the yeast to grow and reproduce.

1 List **three** places where yeast grows naturally.

2 Which gas combines with sugar to give a high energy yield?

3 Explain what is meant by 'anaerobic respiration'.

4 Which type of respiration is needed for yeast cells to grow and reproduce?

yeast fermenting sugar

carbon dioxide   [fermentation products]   ethanol

bread and rolls   wine   spirits   beer

B The products of yeast's anaerobic fermentation are used in food and drink manufacture.

Ethanol is not only a waste product of anaerobic respiration, it is also a toxin to all living cells. As its concentration builds up during anaerobic respiration it kills yeast cells. Ethanol also kills human liver cells if it is consumed in excess.

5 Suggest why:
  a bread does not taste of ethanol
  b most wine isn't fizzy.

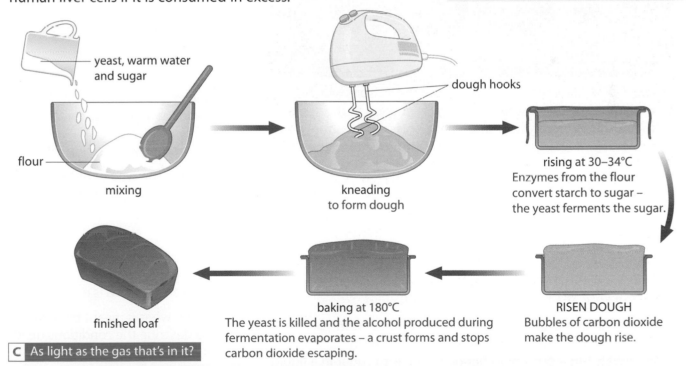

yeast, warm water and sugar

dough hooks

flour

mixing

kneading to form dough

rising at 30–34°C
Enzymes from the flour convert starch to sugar – the yeast ferments the sugar.

finished loaf

baking at 180°C
The yeast is killed and the alcohol produced during fermentation evaporates – a crust forms and stops carbon dioxide escaping.

RISEN DOUGH
Bubbles of carbon dioxide make the dough rise.

C As light as the gas that's in it?

The yeast species *Saccharomyces cerevisiae* is used in bread making. The yeast's function is to ferment sugars present in the flour or added to the dough. Sugars from rice, wheat, barley and corn can be used. The more bubbles of carbon dioxide are trapped in the elastic dough, the more it will rise.

Baker's yeast contains 50% protein, a rich source of vitamin B, niacin and folic acid, and so it is used in the food industry as a supplement to enrich many different products.

6 Explain fully:
  a the link between how much energy is released and how much oxygen is available when yeast respires
  b why yeast cells are killed when making bread and wine
  c why bread dough rises.

Yeast and making alcoholic drinks

By the end of this topic you should be able to:

- describe what the energy source for yeast is in brewing beer and making wine
- explain that alcoholic fermentation is due to the anaerobic respiration of yeast
- describe and explain the stages in brewing and wine making.

Sprouting barley seeds.

Hops.

A Ingredients of beer.

Cereal grains, like those from barley, are seeds from which a new plant can grow. A store of energy is needed in the seeds, so they can start to grow or germinate. This is the carbohydrate starch. Starch is a large insoluble molecule and cannot be transferred from one cell to another. It cannot be used to release energy in mitochondria without first being broken down to sugar.

Amylase enzymes in the seeds convert the starch to the sugar **maltose** when the seeds start to sprout or germinate. This process starts off the production of beer. In beer making it is known as **malting**. Damp barley grains are spread out in a thin layer and kept at a temperature of 10–15°C.

Beer making at a brewery takes place in three enormous containers – a different process takes place in each:

- the **mash tun** – enzymes change starch into sugar in a liquid called the **wort**
- the boiler – flavour from **hops** is added and the wort is sterilised
- the fermenter – yeast uses the sugary solution (wort) as an energy source and ferments it anaerobically, producing ethanol and carbon dioxide.

Pipes connect the containers or vessels to one another and to other equipment such as filters and coolers.

1 Explain:
   a what part of plants cereal grains are
   b what they will develop into.

2 Describe the type of nutrient that starch is and outline its role in seeds.

3 a Describe how starch is turned into sugar in seeds.
   b Explain why this is necessary.

4 Explain what is meant by 'malting' and describe the conditions needed for it to occur.

malt house

Barley seeds germinate.

Enzymes change starch to sugar.

malting

drying → grains crushed →

mash tun

mashing

Enzymes change starch to a sugary liquid called wort.

warm water

wort

filtered

hops · sugar

copper boiler

boiling

2.5 hours

Flavour from hops is added and enzyme action is stopped – wort is sterilised.

filtering and cooling ← wort

fermenter

yeast

fermenting

8 days
3–14°C

Yeast ferments the sugars to ethanol and carbon dioxide.

beer → filtered → other treatments → packaged for sale

B Brewing beer commercially.

Hops are the dried flower heads of a climbing plant. They are specially grown to be used in beer making and to give it its bitter taste. Most of the carbon dioxide produced during fermentation of the wort escapes. Eventually the yeast dies as the level of ethanol increases and the nutrients are used up.

C Ripe grapes have a high sugar content.

At wineries, grapes are crushed and then pressed to release the fruit juice containing the natural sugars. This energy source is easily accessible to the yeast, on the grape skins, to ferment into ethanol and carbon dioxide in a fermenter.

5 a Explain the difference in the processes in the mash tun and the boiler.
  b Where does yeast get the energy it needs during beer production?

6 Describe what hops are and why they are used in brewing beer.

7 Write a word equation for the type of respiration yeast uses during beer production.

8 Suggest what solid is filtered out:
  a before fermentation
  b when the fermentation has finished.

9 Chicha is a fermented drink brewed in South America. It is made from a type of cereal known as yellow maize. Construct and complete a table with two columns to show how the maize will need to be treated to produce Chicha. Head the left-hand column 'Process' and the right-hand column 'Reason'.

Fermenters and penicillin production

By the end of this topic you should be able to:

- describe and explain the features of an industrial fermenter
- describe clearly how very large numbers of microorganisms can be cultured safely
- list the specific needs of the mould *Penicillium* to produce penicillin
- specify when the release of penicillin from *Penicillium* occurs during its growth in the fermenter.

Industrial biotechnology uses enormous culture vessels called fermenters, or bioreactors, to grow microorganisms on a vast scale.

There are two main requirements of fermenters. These are:
- keeping contaminating organisms out
- providing the conditions that allow the desired microorganisms to grow efficiently during the culture period.

Before starting a fermentation, the required microorganisms will have been **isolated** and grown as a pure culture. The pure culture is needed in large amounts. The entire fermenter and all the substances and equipment used during the fermentation must also be sterile.

A Large scale fermentation.

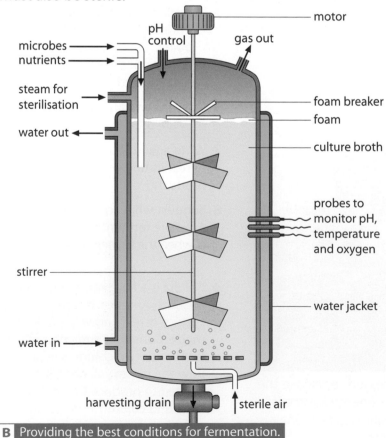

motor
pH control
gas out
microbes
nutrients
steam for sterilisation
water out
foam breaker
foam
culture broth
probes to monitor pH, temperature and oxygen
stirrer
water jacket
water in
harvesting drain
sterile air

B Providing the best conditions for fermentation.

1 a What are the **two** important needs in the design of fermenters?
  b Suggest why each of these is important.

Microbes need to be supplied with nutrients, and some need oxygen, if they are to grow. A carbohydrate source of energy and a source of nitrogen enable them to synthesise protein. The fermenter is stirred continuously to keep the microbes and nutrients in close contact. It also maintains an even temperature throughout the mixture. The optimum growth temperature is about 28°C – it depends on the species of microbe being used. During fermentation the microbes release heat energy and the fermenter needs to be cooled by cold water in the outer jacket.

Sensors inside the fermenter constantly monitor temperature, pH and oxygen concentration. They send information to computer control systems, which can automatically adjust their levels.

The antibiotic **penicillin** can be made in a fermenter by the mould *Penicillium*. The growth medium used contains sugar and other nutrients, such as sources of nitrogen.

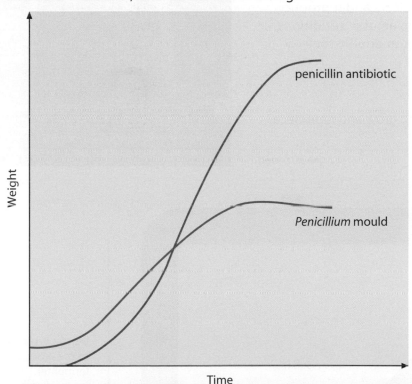

| C | Penicillin is produced when the mould is running out of nutrients. |

Penicillin starts to be secreted into the growth medium only when *Penicillium* has nearly finished its increase in weight. This is when most of the nutrients for growth have been used up. The culture is stopped when the maximum weight of antibiotic is present. Once the growth medium has been filtered off, the antibiotic is extracted from it and crystallised.

6 Where is penicillin found when the fermentation is stopped?

7 List as many things as you can that graph C tells you.

2 Explain why large volumes of sterile air need to be supplied to the aerobic microbes.

3 How is a constant temperature maintained throughout the fermentation?

4 a Suggest why foam develops on the surface of the culture solution.
   b Use diagram B to explain how it is treated during the fermentation.

5 List all the factors which are monitored constantly in the fermenter. Explain why each of these factors must be monitored closely.

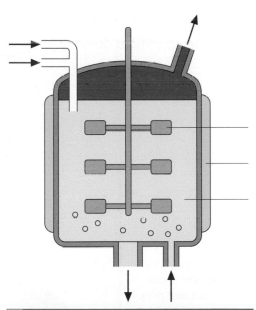

| D | Vertical section through a fermenter. |

8 a Copy and complete diagram D by adding labels to the guide lines and arrows. Include explanations of why certain features are important.
   b Explain what would happen to the fermentation in diagram D if:
     (i) the stirrer stopped working,
     (ii) the airflow decreased by 80%.
     Give a reason for each answer

Mycoprotein by fungal fermentation

By the end of this topic you should be able to:

- define mycoprotein and recall which fungus produces it
- explain that the biomass of fungal hyphae is the product from the fermenter
- describe the conditions needed to produce mycoprotein.

The fungus *Fusarium venenatum* is used in 50 m high fermenters to produce a protein-rich food called mycoprotein. It is suitable for vegetarians.

Fusarium lives naturally in soil, where it feeds on the dead remains of plants and animals. Its fungal body consists of microscopic, narrow, branched, thread-like structures called hyphae. These microscopic fungi grow quickly and reproduce, needing relatively little space. In optimum aerobic conditions, with a plentiful supply of nutrients, they can double their biomass every five hours.

1 Which fungus produces mycoprotein?

2 What conditions does the fungus need to grow and reproduce?

A This fermenter is taller than a stack of 11 double-decker buses and the microscopic fungus *Fusarium venenatum* grows inside it.

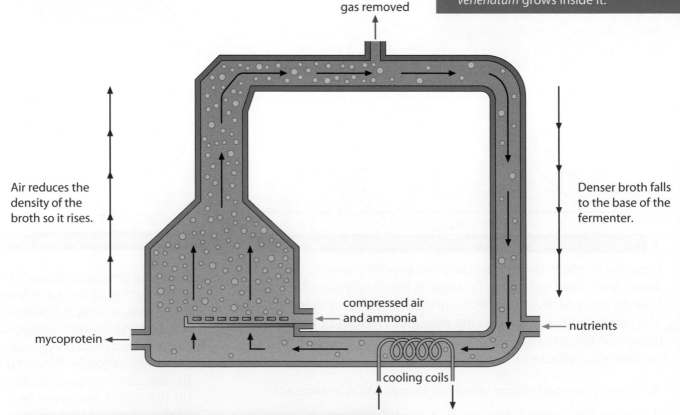

gas removed

Air reduces the density of the broth so it rises.

Denser broth falls to the base of the fermenter.

compressed air and ammonia

nutrients

mycoprotein

cooling coils

B A stream of compressed air provides the agitation in this fermenter.

The mycoprotein fermenter in diagram B has a different design to that described in the previous unit, which used a mechanical stirrer. Here an air lift, or 'loop', fermenter is used. It provides a more gentle agitation process than stirring, and it protects the delicate fungal hyphae which are the final product.

The fermentation process lasts for six weeks and there is a steady input of nutrients into the fermenter during this time to maintain the growth of the fungus. The fungi convert their food to biomass. Starch from potatoes or cereals is used as a source of carbohydrate because it is cheap and so makes the process economical. The starch is treated with enzymes to break it down to glucose before being added to the fermenter. Ammonia is also added as a source of nitrogen. The product here is the whole fungal body of *Fusarium*, or its biomass.

5 a Give **two** nutrients that are added to the fermenter.
 b Explain why they are added throughout the fermentation process.

6 Explain precisely what the product from the fermentation is.

After harvesting from the fermenter, the mycoprotein is dried. At this stage it looks similar to pastry but at the microscopic level the harvested hyphae have a similar form to animal muscle cells. This is because they are both made up of microscopic filaments.

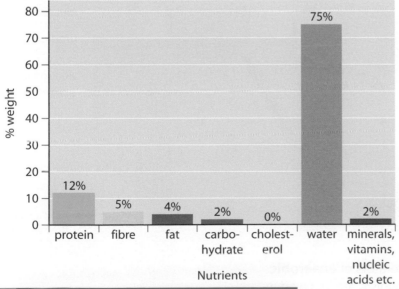

D Nutrient value of freshly harvested mycoprotein.

3 Use diagram B to explain how heat from the aerobic fermentation is prevented from overheating the fermenter so its temperature is a constant 32°C.

4 Describe **two** uses of compressed air in the loop fermenter.

C Flavoured, shaped and packaged mycoprotein.

7 A vegetarian finds it difficult to include enough protein in his diet. Write a fact sheet for him to explain:
 a what mycoprotein is
 b an outline of its production
 c **three** ways that it could be included in his diet.

Biogas

By the end of this topic you should be able to:

- describe how biogas can be produced from plant and animal waste by anaerobic fermentation
- give examples of small- and large-scale biogas production
- evaluate the advantages and disadvantages of the design of biogas generators.

Biogas is produced by anaerobic fermentation of plant material or animal waste, such as manure, **sewage sludge** and kitchen waste. Biogas can only be produced in this way if the waste contains carbohydrates. The fuel or biogas produced is made up mainly of methane with some carbon dioxide. The scale of biogas production can vary from a small household system to large commercial factories.

1 What is biogas?

2 What materials are needed to produce biogas?

3 What biological process is used to make biogas?

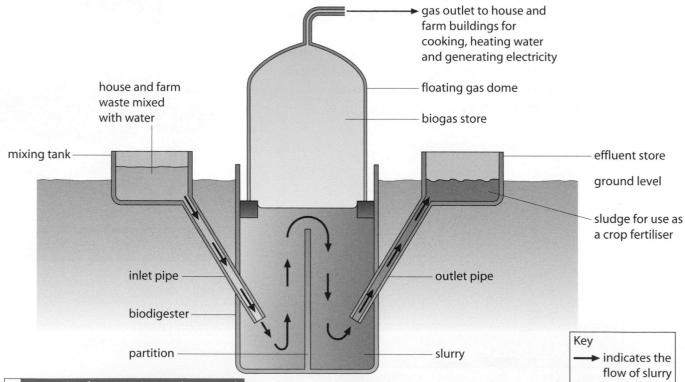

A Anaerobic fermentation underground.

The fermentation takes place in biogas generators or **anaerobic digesters**. Many different types of microorganism are involved in the breakdown of materials into biogas. The simplest types of biogas generators have no moving parts. They are often designed to use animal dung and are suitable for small-scale farms. Gas is fed directly to the farmer's house. Disadvantages of having farm-based biogas generators include having to stock and monitor the biogenerator on a daily basis, using land to house the biogenerator and pipework, and the initial set-up costs.

B What a difference biogas makes.

4 Suggest:
  a **two** uses of the biogas for a farmer's household
  b how the sludge remaining after fermentation is used on the farm
  c how village hygiene will be improved by feeding the biodigester.

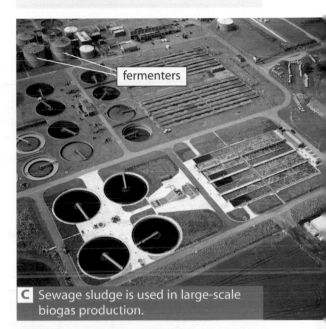

C Sewage sludge is used in large-scale biogas production.

Except in very large systems, biogas production is actually a secondary benefit of using a biogas generator. The primary benefits are nutrient recycling, waste treatment and odour control.

Bioreactors in industrialised countries, such as those in Europe, are usually found above ground. Waste from sugar factories can be used for large-scale biogas generation. To maximise biogas production in a bioreactor some, or all, of the features in Table D can be included in the design of the system.

Feature	Advantage for system	Disadvantage for system
Automatic mixing system in feed tank	Speeds up digestion in the fermenter	Maintenance and energy costs of the mixing equipment
Pumps to force organic matter into the fermenter	Reduces labour and supplies a constant amount of feed to the fermenter	Maintenance and energy costs of the pump
Heating system in the fermenter	Speeds up the fermentation rate and biogas production in temperate climates	Energy costs, especially during cold seasons
Agitation system in the fermenter	Speeds up the fermentation rate as microbes and organic matter are in closer contact	High energy costs and potential for agitator breaking down
Floating gas holder (drum)	Constant gas pressure supplied	Expensive and require intensive maintenance

D Factors affecting the efficiency of bioreactors.

5 a List **three** design features of biogas generators that are advantages because they speed up the fermentation rate.
  b Looking at all the features you have listed, what is a common disadvantage of them?
  c Suggest which design feature would be most useful in a biogas reactor in northern Europe. Explain your answer.

Ethanol-based biofuels

By the end of this topic you should be able to:

- describe how ethanol-based fuels (biofuels) are produced
- interpret economic and environmental data about fuel production by fermentation and the use of these fuels.

Carbohydrate-rich crops such as sugar cane, sugar beet, maize and wheat can be anaerobically fermented into ethanol-based fuels. This is known as **bioethanol** or biofuel because it is produced from living plant material. Starch in the source crop is converted to glucose by the action of carbohydrase enzymes. Yeast is added to ferment the sugars anaerobically to carbon dioxide and ethanol. The ethanol can then be separated by distillation and used as fuel instead of petrol.

1 a Explain what is meant by 'biofuels'.
  b Describe how ethanol-based fuels are made.
  c What are these fuels used for?

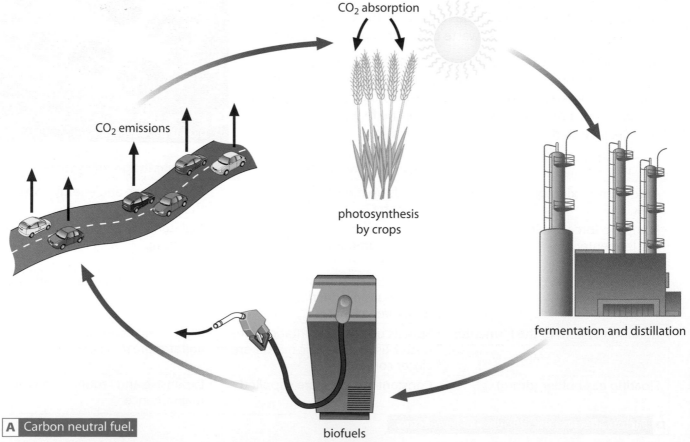

CO₂ absorption

CO₂ emissions

photosynthesis by crops

fermentation and distillation

biofuels

A Carbon neutral fuel.

Ethanol is a 'carbon friendly' or carbon neutral fuel. This term is used because the crops grown to make it remove carbon dioxide from the atmosphere during photosynthesis as they grow. The cars that burn biofuels release carbon dioxide back into the air. This means that there is no *overall* effect on carbon dioxide levels in the atmosphere. Biofuels are also fully renewable and do not deplete the Earth's resources.

2 Explain the concept of carbon neutral fuels.

3 Give another advantage of biofuels.

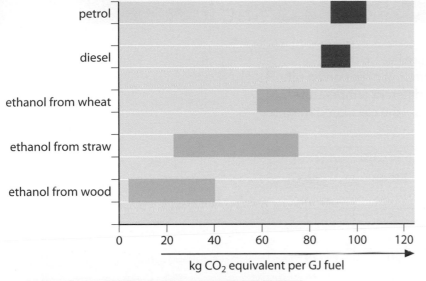

B Greenhouse gas emissions from transport fuels.

Bar chart B shows the carbon dioxide emissions formed when various fuels are used in vehicles. A range of values is given for each type of fuel depending on its manufacture.

An increasing number of governments are encouraging bioethanol production. Bar chart C shows the cost of biofuels and petrol in various countries in euros per litre.

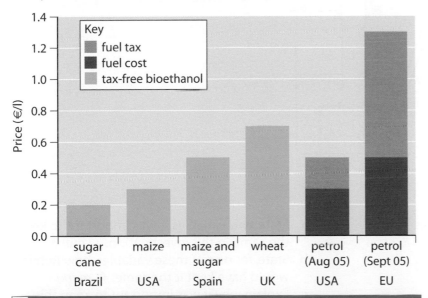

C Production of bioethanol is increasing worldwide because of limited oil reserves, high oil prices and climate change.

In Somerset, Green Spirit Fuels are planning to build a bioethanol plant to produce 131 million litres of ethanol annually from locally grown wheat. Some of the ethanol will be mixed with just 15% petrol to produce a fuel known as E85. **'Flex-fuel'** cars have engines that can run on pure ethanol, pure petrol or any mixture of the two. A computer chip analyses the mixture when the tank is filled and adjusts the engine accordingly.

4 Which fuel produces:
  a the highest carbon dioxide emission
  b the lowest carbon dioxide emission?

5 Which ethanol-based fuel has the highest carbon dioxide emission?

6 a Which fuel is cheapest in the UK?
  b (i) What country produces the cheapest biofuel?
     (ii) What is this fuel made from?
  c Explain why petrol is expensive in Europe.
  d Which crop does the USA use to produce biofuels?
  e What is the price difference in euros per litre of biofuel in Brazil and the UK?

7 a Suggest **one** environmental reason and **one** economic reason why the UK government is encouraging biofuel production.
  b Explain how sugar beet and wheat can be turned into transport fuels.
  c Describe the content of E85 fuel and explain how it is that either E85 or normal petrol can be used in some new cars.

Investigative Skills Assessment

Romin investigated what effect temperature has on the fermentation of yeast. He measured the amount of gas given off. He used a 5% glucose solution and three different temperatures. Each experiment was repeated three times – the calculated means are shown below.

Time (minutes) after gas first released	Volume of gas collected (cm³)		
	28°C	30°C	32°C
2	1	2	3
4	2	5	12
6	4	13	20
8	7	20	28
10	10	28	36
12	17	35	41

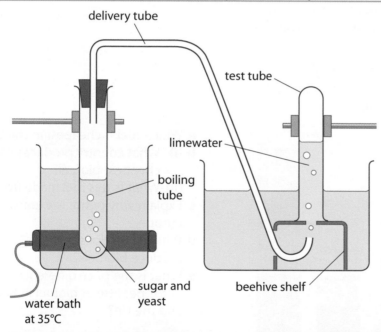

1 What was Romin trying to find out in his investigation? *(2 marks)*

2 Which is the dependent variable in the investigation? *(1 mark)*

3 a What range of values was used for the independent variable? *(1 mark)*
  b How could the reliability of the results be checked? *(1 mark)*

4 a Which results are anomalous? If you think that there are none then include this in your answer. *(1 mark)*
  b Explain **one** possible cause of error in the investigation. *(1 mark)*

5 a State **two** variables it was important to keep the same in this investigation. *(2 marks)*
  b State, for **one** of these variables, how Romin would have kept it the same. *(1 mark)*
  c Explain why it was important to keep this variable constant. *(1 mark)*

6 ✎ What conclusion can be made from Romin's results? *(2 marks)*

7 Present the results of this investigation in a suitable format. *(4 marks)*

Glossary

abdomen Lower part of the trunk of the body, containing most of the digestive system.

abiogenesis The mistaken belief that living organisms could come into existence from non-living matter.

H **active transport** Transport of substances across a partially permeable membrane against a concentration gradient, using energy from respiration.

aerobic respiration Respiration which requires the presence of oxygen – the release of energy from glucose using oxygen from air.

agar A nutrient-rich jelly used to grow microbes on.

alveoli Small air sacs in the lungs where exchange of gases with blood occurs. (single: alveolus)

amylase Carbohydrase enzyme that converts starch to maltose.

anaerobic digester A fermenter in which anaerobic fermentation occurs.

anaerobic respiration Respiration which takes place in the absence of oxygen – the release of energy from glucose without using oxygen. **H** Lactic acid is a waste product in animals.

arteries Large blood vessels that carry blood away from the heart.

aseptic No unwanted microorganisms are present.

autoclave A device used for sterilising laboratory equipment with superheated steam.

bioethanol Alcohol produced from plant material, by fermentation – it is used as fuel.

biogas A mixture of mostly methane and carbon dioxide, formed during anaerobic fermentation of animal and plant wastes.

biogenesis Living organisms produce other living organisms.

bioreactor A vessel where fermentation takes place.

bronchi Tubes in the lungs leading to alveoli.

broth A nutrient liquid used to culture microbes.

budding Asexual reproduction of yeast.

capillaries Very small blood vessels with thin walls – they penetrate almost all tissues and exchange substances with cells.

cell theory All cells come from pre-existing cells.

concentration gradient Caused by the difference in concentration of a substance in two solutions either side of a partially permeable membrane.

culture medium A nutrient-rich jelly or liquid that microbes can grow in.

curds Solid white particles formed when milk curdles.

dialyser Machine containing dialysing fluid, used to exchange substances with blood during dialysis.

diaphragm Muscular membrane below the lungs and heart but above the stomach, used in breathing.

diffusion Movement by random motion from an area of high concentration to an area of lower concentration.

digest Break down into smaller parts, such as food in the gut.

dilate Get wider.

ethanol Product of anaerobic respiration by microbes.

fatigue Tire and lose level of response, as in muscles during extended vigorous activity.

fermentation Anaerobic respiration by microorganisms.

fermenter Vessel in which microorganisms are cultured so that they produce something humans want.

flex fuel A vehicle that can use any ratio of an ethanol: petrol mixture as fuel.

germinate Sprouting of seeds.

glomerulus Capillary network at the start of a kidney tubule, where blood is filtered.

glycogen Substance made from glucose, stored in muscle and liver cells for times of low glucose availability from the blood, such as vigorous exercise.

guard cells Cells that surround the stomata in a plant's leaf surface and control its opening and closing.

haemodialysis Dialysis of the blood using a dialyser with an artificial membrane.

haemoglobin Red substance in red blood cells, combines with oxygen to form oxyhaemoglobin.

hops Dried flower heads of a climbing plant used to flavour beer.

immunosuppressant drug Drug that suppresses the reaction of the immune system, used to prevent rejection of transplanted organs such as kidneys.

isolated Separated from other microorganisms.

kidney failure When less than 30% of the kidneys are functioning as normal.

H **lactic acid** Substance produced from the incomplete breakdown of glucose during anaerobic respiration.

lactose Sugar found in milk.

malting Conversion of starch to maltose by enzymes in germinating barley seeds.

maltose Sugar formed from starch by amylase.

mash tun A large vessel in a brewery where sugar is extracted from crushed barley grains.

microvilli Fine extensions of the surface membrane of cells that line the small intestine.

mycoprotein A high protein vegetarian food made of fungal biomass – it is grown in a fermenter.

osmosis The net movement of water across a partially permeable membrane from a dilute solution to a concentrated solution.

oxygen debt The oxygen that is required after vigorous activity to convert lactic acid back to glucose.

oxyhaemoglobin Haemoglobin that is combined with oxygen.

partially permeable membrane Membrane that has pores which let small particles through but not large ones.

penicillin An antibiotic produced from the fungus *Penicillium*.

plasma Watery part of the blood.

potometer Apparatus used to measure the rate of transpiration in a plant.

pure culture A culture containing only one type of microorganism.

red blood cells Cells in blood that contain haemoglobin.

rejection When the body reacts against a transplant and kills it.

rennin An enzyme used in cheese-making.

root hair cells Cells on roots with long extensions which increase the surface area for absorption.

sewage sludge The precipitate left at the sewage works after water treatment.

spontaneous generation The mistaken belief that living organisms could come into existence from non-living matter.

starter A culture of bacteria added to milk to produce yoghurt or cheese.

stomata Tiny holes in the surface of leaves for the exchange of gases between the air spaces inside the leaf and the air outside. (single: stoma)

strain A type of microorganism within a species.

swan-neck flask A flask with a narrow S-shaped neck.

thorax Top part of the trunk of the body, containing the lungs and heart, protected by the rib cage.

tissue type The type of tissue defined by the cell markers on the cells in the tissue.

transpiration Evaporation of water, mostly from the leaves of a plant.

transplant Placing an organ from one person into another person's body.

tubules Fine tubes in the kidney that exchange substances with the blood.

urea Waste product in the body excreted in urine through the kidneys.

urine Liquid that is left in kidney tubules after all the substances that the body needs have been reabsorbed.

veins Large blood vessels that carry blood back to the heart.

villi Finger-like extensions of the small intestine wall.

whey The watery liquid formed when milk curdles.

wilt Lose water and go floppy, as when plants lose too much water by transpiration.

wort A sugary liquid found in brewing beer.

xylem Tubes that carry water through a plant.

1 The table shows Marie's results after investigating the effect of exercise on her heart rate. She measured her heart rate immediately after sitting, walking or jogging for 2 minutes. She carried out each test three times, and left 2 minutes rest between each test. Her heart rate is given in beats per minute.

Exercise	Sitting			Walking			Jogging		
	1	2	3	1	2	3	1	2	3
Heart rate	71	68	72	91	85	84	113	110	119

a Explain why Marie took three measurements for each kind of exercise. *(1 mark)*

b Calculate the average for each level of exercise. *(1 mark)*

c Explain what Marie's results show. *(1 mark)*

d Phil's results for the same investigation were: sitting 62, walking 84; jogging 108. Give **one** reason for the difference between Phil's and Marie's results. Explain your answer. *(2 marks)*

2 The diagram shows a simplified plan of the human circulatory system.

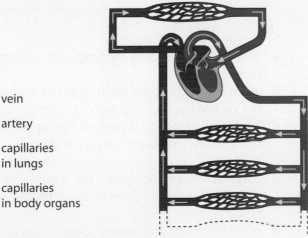

vein

artery

capillaries in lungs

capillaries in body organs

A Human circulatory system.

a Sketch the diagram and draw appropriate lines from the labels to the diagram. *(2 marks)*

b Explain how you chose where to label the artery. *(1 mark)*

c In which kind of blood vessel – artery, capillary or vein – does most exchange of substances occur? *(1 mark)*

d Explain how this kind of blood vessel is adapted for exchange. *(1 mark)*

3 Graph B shows the rate of transpiration from a plant on a warm summer day in the UK.

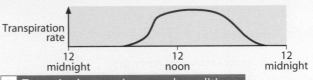

Transpiration rate

12 midnight   12 noon   12 midnight

B Transpiration rate in normal conditions.

a Explain the shape of graph B. *(2 marks)*

b Suggest how the data for the graph were collected. *(1 mark)*

Graph C shows the rate of transpiration from the same plant a few days later when it was cool and rainy.

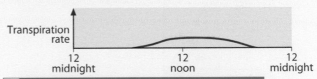

Transpiration rate

12 midnight   12 noon   12 midnight

C Transpiration rate in cool, rainy conditions.

c Give **two** reasons to explain the difference between graph C and graph B. *(2 marks)*

d At the same time as the data for graph B were collected, the data for a plant normally found in very dry regions were also collected. Sketch a graph to show the rate of transpiration from this plant. Explain the differences between your graph and graph B. *(2 marks)*

4 Graph D shows the different sources of energy used by muscle cells as the effort put into exercise increases.

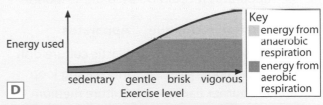

Energy used

sedentary   gentle   brisk   vigorous
Exercise level

D

Key
■ energy from anaerobic respiration
■ energy from aerobic respiration

a Explain why the energy from aerobic respiration levels off as effort increases. *(1 mark)*

b Write a word equation for anaerobic respiration. *(1 mark)*

c Anaerobic respiration produces less energy per glucose molecule than aerobic respiration. Explain why. *(1 mark)*

d Describe what happens to the product of anaerobic respiration after exercise has ended. *(2 marks)*

e Explain what is meant by the term 'oxygen debt'. *(2 marks)*

5 In school laboratories microorganisms can be cultured safely using the aseptic technique.

   a What types of cultures are produced using this technique? *(1 mark)*

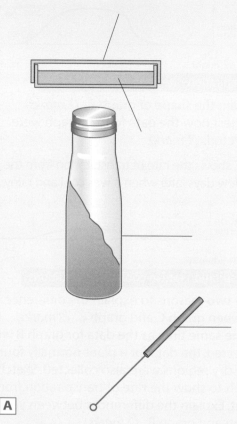

A

   b Add labels to the guidelines on the apparatus above. *(2 marks)*

   c Match each sterilisation technique with the apparatus it could be used on. *(3 marks)*

Sterilisation technique	Apparatus
Pressurised steam	Plastic culture dish
Ultraviolet light	Inoculating loop
Bunsen burner flame	Culture medium

6 a Describe how Spallanzani's experiment with chicken broth challenged the theory of 'spontaneous generation'. *(1 mark)*

   b What is meant by 'biogenesis'? *(1 mark)*

   c Under three headings – apparatus, method and results – explain how Pasteur totally refuted the theory of 'spontaneous generation'. *(3 marks)*

7 Sara carried out an investigation into yoghurt production. A pH sensor was used in the culture mixture during a two-hour period while the yoghurt was forming. The results can be seen on the graph below.

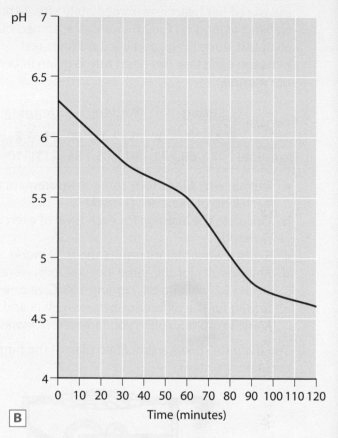

B

   a What are the two main ingredients in yoghurt? *(1 mark)*

   b What is the pH of the mixture at the start and at the end of the investigation? *(1 mark)*

   c Explain the biological process taking place in the mixture that leads to the pH change. *(3 marks)*

   d Suggest what temperature the mixture should be kept at when yoghurt is being produced. *(1 mark)*

   e What control experiment should be set up to validate the results? *(1 mark)*

8 a Name **one** biofuel and the type of fermentation that produces it. *(2 marks)*

   b Draw and fully label a diagram to illustrate the carbon-neutral concept of biofuels. *(3 marks)*

Analysing substances

A Where does all the water that we use come from?

We all assume that when we turn on a tap, water will come out of it. Industry depends upon large amounts of water, mainly for cooling, but also for washing and as a solvent. For example, 350 litres of water are needed to make a litre of beer, and 200 litres of water are needed to produce one newspaper.

In this country, each of us uses about 180 litres of water every day. After being stored in a reservoir, this water must be purified so that it is made safe to drink. Its purity is then checked using modern computerised analysis techniques.

By the end of this unit you should be able to:

- describe what is in the water we drink and how it can be made as pure as possible
- describe what strong and weak alkalis are
- **H** evaluate the contributions of Arrhenius, Brønsted and Lowry to our understanding of acid–base behaviour
- describe how we can identify and analyse solutions using modern techniques.

1 The list gives some uses of water in the home:

baths and showers; clothes washing; cooking; dish washing; drinking; flushing the toilet; gardening; washing the car

a Sort them in order, showing which you think are the most important. Put the most important use first.

b Explain why you have ordered them in this way.

The water cycle

By the end of this topic you should be able to:

- explain how water is cycled by a continuous process involving evaporation, condensation and precipitation.

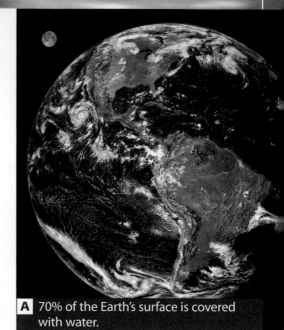

A 70% of the Earth's surface is covered with water.

4500 million years ago the Earth was a mass of molten rock. Over millions of years it cooled down so that the surface temperature fell below 100°C. Water vapour from early volcanoes condensed to form liquid water, and the first rivers, lakes and oceans were formed.

The **water cycle** describes how there is a constant exchange of water between the surface of the Earth and the atmosphere. The Sun heats water so that it evaporates. This water vapour then rises because hot gases are less dense than cool ones. As the water vapour rises it cools down so that it condenses into water droplets in clouds. These clouds cool even more and produce rain or snow.

As air rises it cools, so water vapour in it condenses to form clouds.

As water droplets get too large and heavy they fall as rain or snow.

Water evaporates from oceans, lakes and rivers to form water vapour.

river
lake
ocean
river
Rivers flow into lakes and eventually the water returns to the oceans.
groundwater

B The water cycle.

Of all of the water on Earth, only 1% can be used. Of the remaining water, 2% is frozen as icebergs and glaciers, and 97% is sea water which is undrinkable. Table C shows the difference in composition between sea water and fresh water.

Ion	Concentration in sea water (mol/dm³)	Concentration in fresh water (mol/dm³)
Sodium (Na⁺)	0.47	0.000 27
Calcium (Ca²⁺)	0.01	0.000 38
Magnesium (Mg²⁺)	0.054	0.000 17
Chloride (Cl⁻)	0.55	0.000 22
Sulfate (SO₄²⁻)	0.038	0.000 12
Hydrogencarbonate (HCO₃⁻)	0.002	0.000 96

C Concentrations of ions in sea water and fresh water.

In the UK, changes in our lifestyle have caused our demand for water to double in the last 50 years. This demand is particularly high in the south-east of England, which is also one of the driest parts of the country. In the very hot summer of 2006, this resulted in a shortage of water and hosepipe bans. Global warming has also led to rising temperatures and an increased demand for water. Some predictions suggest that the average annual temperature could increase by up to 4.5°C by 2080. Water companies are always looking at ways of conserving water.

1 Which two ions are most common in:
   a sea water?
   b fresh water?

2 a Add up the total amount of ions in each type of water.
   b Why do you think that there is a difference?

3 Suggest how we could obtain drinking water from sea water.

D In times of severe water shortages, people have to fetch water from standpipes in the road.

Some estimates suggest that by 2025, 50% of the world's population will live in areas where there is not enough water. However, demand for water globally continues to grow by 2–3% each year. This is mainly due to increasing industrialisation in developing countries.

4 What changes in lifestyle have led to an increased demand for water?

5 What effect would new housing developments in the south-east have on the demand for water?

6 List three ways in which you could try to conserve water.

7 How would the water cycle change as more and more water is needed?

Purifying our water

By the end of this topic you should be able to:

- explain that our water must be of the correct quality with sufficiently low levels of dissolved salts and microorganisms
- explain how this is achieved by filtration and chlorination
- describe how water filters remove dissolved substances from tap water
- describe how pure water is produced by distillation.

A Intake of water from a river.

Our tap water comes originally from either the ground or rivers. Water underground is stored in aquifers, which are layers of rock that can absorb water. This water can be removed by drilling into the rock layer, and then pumping it out.

Water from rivers flows through a series of screens which filter out sticks, leaves and other large debris. This water, or water from aquifers, is then mixed with ozone. This removes algae and some polluting pesticides and kills about 99% of the bacteria. Unreacted ozone is destroyed. Smaller solid impurities are removed by filtration through sand and gravel. This removes the larger molecules from the smaller solid impurities. The water is then passed through granules of activated carbon in **filter beds**. The carbon has a very large surface area (half a teaspoon has the surface area of a football pitch) so is an effective filter for remaining pesticides. After filtration the water is then **chlorinated**, which kills any remaining bacteria. Excess chlorine is removed chemically. The purified water is finally stored in covered reservoirs with a tiny amount of chlorine left in it, to make sure that the water is still free of bacteria when it reaches our taps.

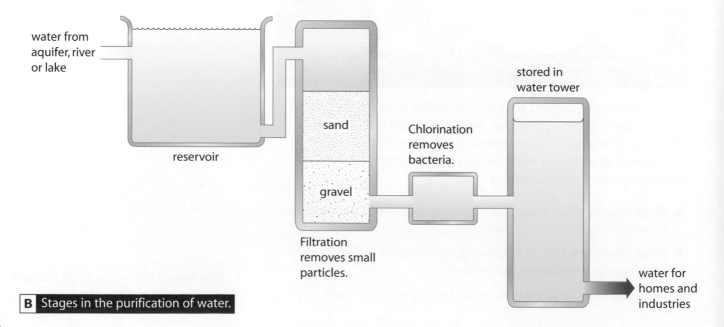

water from aquifer, river or lake

reservoir

sand

gravel

Filtration removes small particles.

Chlorination removes bacteria.

stored in water tower

water for homes and industries

B Stages in the purification of water.

Some people do not like the taste or smell of tap water, so they use **water filters**. These contain ion-exchange columns which remove dissolved ions like magnesium, calcium, lead and aluminium. They also contain carbon and silver, which remove chlorine and any organic molecules in sediment that has come from the water pipes. The taste and quality of the water are improved, although the cartridges in filters need to be replaced regularly so that they remain efficient. However, some people think that drinking water without minerals can harm our health, since calcium ions in particular are needed for good health.

4 Give two advantages and two disadvantages of using water filters.

5 Where have the dissolved ions come from?

An alternative is to distil tap water. Water distillers for the home are available, producing about 1 litre of distilled water per hour. Water distilled in these devices leaves behind dissolved salts, pesticides and harmful microorganisms.

C An alternative method of purifying water at home

6 Would a water filter or a water distiller be more economic to run? Explain your answer.

1 Why is the water obtained from an aquifer purer than that obtained from a river?

2 Suggest how pesticides and other pollutants get into river water.

3 Why does a large surface area give effective filtration?

7 Devise a presentation describing the purification of water, both on a large scale and at home.

Solubility

By the end of this topic you should be able to:

- describe which types of substances are soluble and which are insoluble in water
- describe how solubility is expressed
- describe how the solubility of gases changes as the temperature changes
- give some examples of how solubility changes with temperature and pressure.

Water is an excellent **solvent**. Most ionic compounds are soluble in water, while many molecular covalent compounds are insoluble in water. There are, however, always exceptions to this rule.

A Copper sulfate is a very soluble ionic compound.

Substance	Type of substance	Mass of substance that dissolves in 100 g of water at 20°C (g)
Sodium chloride	ionic	36.0
Calcium carbonate	ionic	insoluble
Copper sulfate	ionic	20.7
Sugar	covalent	204
Oxygen	covalent	0.004
Hexane	covalent	insoluble

B Solubilities of some ionic and covalent substances.

The **solubility** of a **solute** in water, or any other solvent, is usually given in grams of solute per 100 g of water (or solvent) at a given temperature.

1 Look at Table B. Which two compounds are exceptions to the general rule about solubility?

2 158 g of potassium nitrate dissolves in 500 g of water. What is its solubility in grams per 100 g of water?

Looking at solubility

Many gases are slightly soluble in water. Their solubility increases as the temperature decreases and as the pressure increases. This is shown on graph C.

3 a What is the approximate solubility of oxygen at (i) 30°C, and (ii) 40°C?
  b What would happen to the amount of oxygen dissolved in water during a very hot summer?

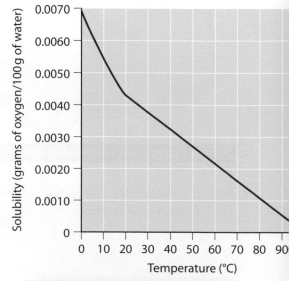

C The solubility of oxygen in water.

Dissolved oxygen is essential for aquatic life. If the temperature of the water increases, the amount of oxygen that is dissolved in it decreases. This can happen near power stations that use a lot of water for cooling. If the heated water is put into rivers, the river water warms up and less oxygen dissolves.

4 Why are few fish found near the outlets from power stations?

The solubility of gases also increases if the pressure increases. This is shown in graph E.

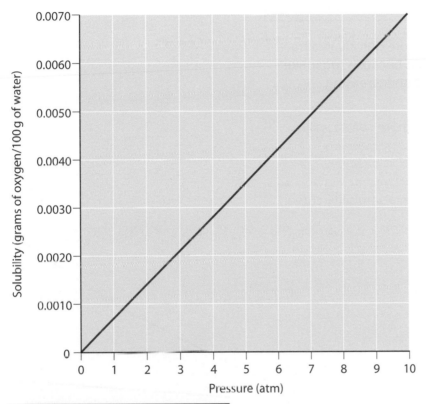

E The effect of pressure on solubility.

D Salmon need high levels of dissolved oxygen. They cannot survive if the water is too warm.

Dissolving carbon dioxide in water under high pressure makes carbonated water. When the bottle is opened, the pressure is released. As the carbon dioxide becomes less soluble it bubbles out of the solution. Carbonated water is often used to make fizzy drinks.

F Releasing the pressure of the gas.

5 How will the solubility of gases change 100 metres below the surface of the sea?

6 Will a can of Coke that has been kept in the fridge produce more or fewer bubbles than one kept at room temperature?

7 Explain why you should never put a goldfish into cooled boiled water.

Saturated solutions

By the end of this topic you should be able to:

- describe how the solubility of solid solutes increases as the temperature increases
- explain that a saturated solution is one in which no more solute will dissolve at that temperature
- interpret solubility curves and explain when crystallisation will occur.

We all know that sugar dissolves much more quickly in a hot cup of tea than in a cold cup of tea. This is because sugar, like nearly all solid solutes, dissolves better with increasing temperature.

A **saturated solution** is one in which no more solute will dissolve at that temperature.

Using solubility curves

The solubility of solids can be shown using a solubility curve.

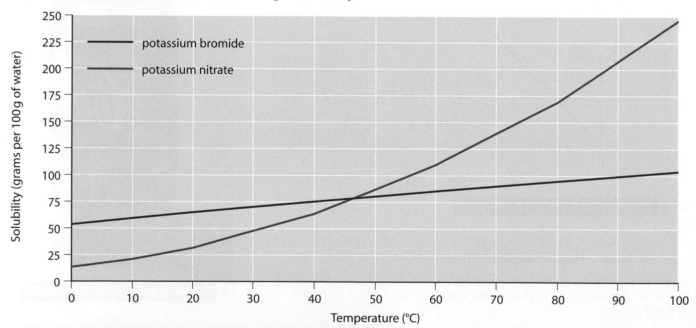

— potassium bromide
— potassium nitrate

B Solubility curves for potassium bromide and potassium nitrate.

Use graph B to answer these questions.

1 Which of the two solutes shown in the graph is more soluble at 20°C?

2 Which is more soluble at 80°C?

3 At about what temperature do the two solutes have the same solubility?

4 How much potassium bromide dissolves in 200 g of water at 60°C?

5 How much water is needed to dissolve 440 g of potassium nitrate at 60°C?

Solubility curves can be used in several ways. Here are some examples.

- To find the mass of a solute that will dissolve in a different amount of water. For example, if 65.2 g of potassium bromide dissolves in 100 g of water at 20°C, 1000 g of water will dissolve 652 g of potassium bromide at the same temperature.
- To find the minimum amount of water needed to dissolve a certain amount of solute at a given temperature. For example, if 31.6 g of potassium nitrate dissolves in 100 g of water at 20°C, 63.2 g of potassium nitrate will need (63.2 / 31.6) * 100 = 200 g of water.
- To predict when solutes will crystallise out of solution.

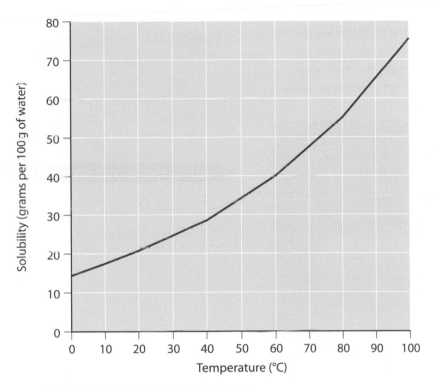

C The solubility curve for copper sulfate.

Graph C shows you that 55.0 g of copper sulfate dissolves in water at 80°C. However, at 20°C only 20.7 g of copper sulfate will dissolve. So if you started with a saturated solution of copper sulfate at 80°C and cooled it, the excess solid will crystallise out. As 55.0 g were dissolved at 80°C but only 20.7 g are soluble at 20°C, the amount of copper sulfate that will crystallise out is 55.0 – 20.7 = 34.3 g.

6 At about what temperature will a solution of copper sulfate containing 50 g in 100 g of water start to form crystals?

7 What mass of crystals will be formed if 100 g of solution containing 40 g of copper sulfate at 60°C is cooled down to 10°C?

D Crystals of copper sulfate have formed as the solution cooled down.

8 Write a quick guide called 'How to use solubility curves'.

Hard water

By the end of this topic you should be able to:

- describe the effect of both hard and soft water on soap
- explain that hard water contains dissolved compounds, usually of magnesium or calcium, which have dissolved when the water came into contact with rocks.

Rain water does not contain any dissolved salts. However, as it seeps through the ground it comes into contact with rocks and dissolves compounds from them. These compounds often contain calcium or magnesium ions, both of which lead to **hard water**.

Anyone living in a hard water area will notice that the water does not easily form lather with soap. Instead a grey scum is formed, so more soap is needed to form lather. In areas where there is **soft water** there are no dissolved compounds and the water readily forms lather with soap.

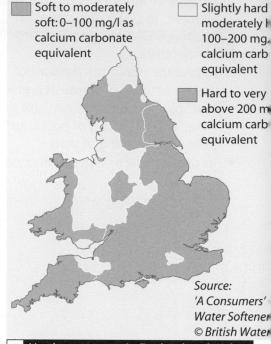

- Soft to moderately soft: 0–100 mg/l as calcium carbonate equivalent
- Slightly hard moderately h 100–200 mg calcium carb equivalent
- Hard to very above 200 m calcium carb equivalent

Source: 'A Consumers' Water Softener © British Water

A Hard water areas in England and Wales.

B The effect of soap on hard and soft water.

1 How do dissolved salts get into water?

2 How could you check if you have hard water at home?

The calcium and magnesium ions that cause hard water are not removed when water is purified at the water works, so they are found in tap water. One of the compounds in soap is called sodium stearate, which is soluble in water. However, when soap reacts with hard water, the sodium stearate reacts with the calcium or magnesium ions in the water to form insoluble calcium stearate or magnesium stearate. This is what is in the scum formed:

calcium ions from water + stearate ions from soap → calcium stearate (scum)
    (soluble)   (soluble)   (insoluble)

We can show which ions are present in hard water by adding small amounts of salt solutions to soap solution. If the water is hard, a scum forms when the mixture is shaken. If the water is soft, lather forms at once. Table C shows typical results.

Solution added	Ions present	Reaction with soap solution
Sodium chloride	Na^+ and Cl^-	lather
Sodium sulfate	Na^+ and SO_4^{2-}	lather
Calcium chloride	Ca^{2+} and Cl^-	scum
Calcium sulfate	Ca^{2+} and SO_4^{2-}	scum
Magnesium chloride	Mg^{2+} and Cl^-	scum
Magnesium sulfate	Mg^{2+} and SO_4^{2-}	scum

C Effect of adding different salts to soap solution.

3 Which ions are responsible for hard water?

4 What is scum?

5 Strontium is in the same group as calcium and magnesium in the Periodic Table. Would you expect its compounds to produce hard water? Explain your answer.

The amount of hardness in water is measured as 'calcium carbonate equivalent'. Although calcium carbonate is insoluble, and therefore not present in our water, the main cause of hardness is calcium hydrogencarbonate. When this is heated it forms calcium carbonate. Calcium carbonate equivalent can therefore be used as an indication of the hardness of water. Its units are mg/dm^3 of water.

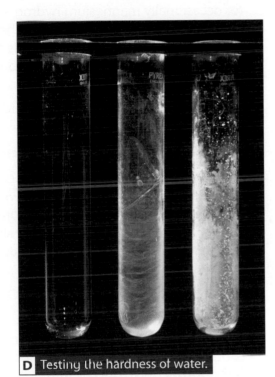

D Testing the hardness of water.

Type of water	Calcium carbonate equivalent (mg/dm^3)
Soft	0–75
Moderately hard	76–150
Hard	151–300
Very hard	300

E Definitions of water hardness.

6 What is calcium carbonate equivalent?

7 Write an encyclopedia entry titled 'Hard water'.

Types of hard water

By the end of this topic you should be able to:

- explain how hard water is formed
- explain the difference between permanently and temporarily hard water.

All hard water contains calcium or magnesium ions dissolved in it. However, depending on the type of rocks that the rain water has run through, two different types of hard water are found.

Most hard water contains soluble **calcium hydrogencarbonate** (or occasionally magnesium hydrogencarbonate). This is formed when carbon dioxide in the atmosphere reacts with rain water to form a slightly acidic solution. This then reacts with calcium carbonate in limestone or chalk to form calcium hydrogencarbonate:

A Water runs through these limestone rocks, and reacts to form temporarily hard water.

calcium carbonate + carbon dioxide + water → calcium hydrogencarbonate

$$CaCO_3(s) + CO_2(g) + H_2O(l) \rightarrow Ca(HCO_3)_2(aq)$$

Magnesium carbonate, found in a few rocks, reacts in a similar way.

Water containing calcium hydrogencarbonate (or magnesium hydrogencarbonate) forms a scum with soap, as it contains dissolved calcium (or magnesium) ions. However, if this water is heated, for example in a kettle, the calcium hydrogencarbonate decomposes to form insoluble calcium carbonate, carbon dioxide and water:

$$Ca(HCO_3)_2(aq) \rightarrow CaCO_3(s) + CO_2(g) + H_2O(l)$$

This means that the calcium ions are no longer in solution, and the hardness has been removed from the water. Water containing calcium hydrogencarbonate is said to be **temporarily hard**. The calcium carbonate formed appears as **limescale** in kettles or hot water systems.

1 **a** Write the word equation for the reaction between magnesium carbonate, carbon dioxide and water.
 b Write a balanced symbol equation for this reaction.

B Limescale build-up in kettles wastes energy.

2 Why has boiling removed the hardness from this type of water?

3 Why would limescale on the heating element make a kettle less efficient?

Rocks like anhydrite and gypsum contain **calcium sulfate**. This is slightly soluble in water, so some of this salt dissolves in the water. Water with calcium sulfate dissolved in it is said to be **permanently hard**. This water cannot be softened by heating.

We can see the effect of boiling temporarily hard water by reacting unboiled and boiled water with soap solution.

soap solution in burette

water sample

C Comparing the hardness of water.

The same volume of water is used in each experiment. Soap solution is added, 1 cm³ at a time, and the water shaken vigorously after each addition to see if a permanent lather forms. Table D shows some sample results.

Type of water	Volume of soap needed to form a permanent lather (cm³)
Unboiled temporarily hard water	6.3
Boiled temporarily hard water	0.7
Distilled water	0.2

D Results from water hardness experiment.

4 What does this experiment show you?

5 Why was distilled water used?

6 What was the only variable in this experiment?

7 What types of values for the amount of soap used would you expect with
   a soft water?
   b permanently hard water?

8 Draw a table showing the similarities and differences between permanently and temporarily hard water.

Removing hardness from water

By the end of this topic you should be able to:

- describe the advantages to health of drinking hard water
- explain the disadvantages of using hard water
- describe how to remove the hardness from water.

The major problem with hard water is that it adds expense to our everyday lives. Hard water forms a scum with soap, so more soap is needed to form lather and allow the soap to act in removing dirt.

Temporarily hard water decomposes when heated, to form calcium carbonate. While this removes calcium ions and thus hardness from the water, they are converted into insoluble calcium carbonate, which forms limescale. This limescale coats the inside of kettles, hot water pipes and boilers, which reduces the efficiency of heating systems.

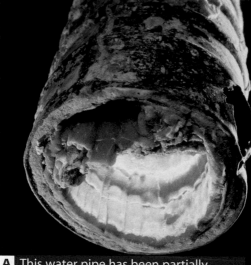

A This water pipe has been partially blocked with limescale.

1 Write a word equation showing what happens when calcium hydrogencarbonate is heated.

2 How does hard water add to expense?

Hard water does have benefits too, since calcium compounds are good for our health. They help to build strong bones and teeth, and also help to prevent heart disease. It has been found that heart disease is more common in soft water areas.

3 a List two advantages of hard water.
   b List two disadvantages of hard water.

Because hard water causes so many problems with heating and washing, some people choose to **soften** their water. This can be done in one of two ways, both of which remove the dissolved calcium and magnesium ions.

Sodium carbonate (Na_2CO_3), sold as 'washing soda', reacts with the calcium or magnesium ions, forming calcium carbonate or magnesium carbonate.

calcium ions + sodium carbonate $\rightarrow$ sodium ions + calcium carbonate

B A cheap and controllable method of softening water.

The more expensive alternative is to install a water softener. These contain an **ion exchange column**, which contains sodium ions (bought as salt). The sodium ions swap places with the calcium and magnesium ions in the hard water, so that the calcium and magnesium ions are removed from the water. However, the water that comes out of a water softener now contains sodium ions which are not good for our health. You should avoid drinking softened water, since too many sodium ions can lead to high blood pressure and heart problems.

Dishwashers have a similar system to water softeners, which is why they must have salt added to them.

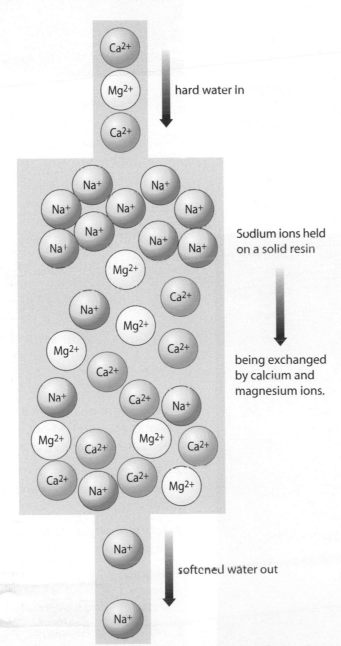

hard water in

Sodium ions held on a solid resin

being exchanged by calcium and magnesium ions.

softened water out

C Exchanging calcium and magnesium ions by sodium ions.

4 a Write a word equation showing the reaction between magnesium sulfate ($MgSO_4$) and sodium carbonate.
 b Write a balanced equation for this reaction.

5 What would be the effect of soap solution on water that had been through an ion exchange column?

6 Why must houses with water softeners also have a tap delivering unsoftened water?

7 Your grandmother lives in a hard water area and complains about the limescale that builds up around the taps in her kitchen. Write a letter explaining the advantages and disadvantages of living in a hard water area. Also explain to her how she could get rid of the hardness if she wanted to.

Flame tests

By the end of this topic you should be able to:

- describe how flame tests can be used to identify metal ions
- know the flame colours for lithium, sodium, potassium, calcium and barium compounds.

Using the results of chemical tests

When potassium is placed in water, it burns with a lilac flame. This lilac colour is characteristic for potassium.

However, very few metals react with water in this way, and metal compounds certainly don't. Analysts use **flame tests** as an alternative method of identifying metal ions in compounds. They use a wire made of nichrome, which is a very unreactive alloy of nickel and chromium, or one made of platinum. The wire is cleaned by dipping it into concentrated hydrochloric acid and then holding it in a blue Bunsen burner flame. This cleaning process is repeated until the wire no longer gives a yellow flame in the Bunsen burner flame. The wire is then dipped into the acid and then into a tiny sample of the solid that is being tested. It is then held back in the flame.

A Potassium reacts with water to form a lilac flame.

B Potassium compounds all have this characteristic lilac flame colour.

1 Why might analysts at a water works want to find out which metal ions are in a sample of water?

2 What must be done to the water sample before it can undergo a flame test?

3 Suggest why nichrome is preferred to platinum.

4 Suggest why the wire must be cleaned before it is placed in the sample being investigated.

5 What would happen to the wire if it was held in a yellow Bunsen burner flame?

Different metal ions produce different coloured flames. This is particularly important for the metals in Groups 1 and 2 of the Periodic Table. All of their compounds are white, so the different flame colours help to distinguish them.

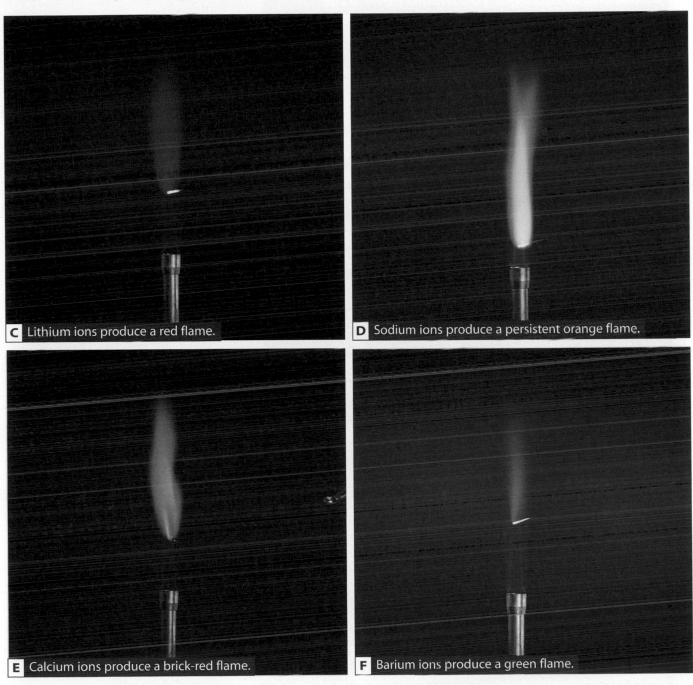

C Lithium ions produce a red flame.

D Sodium ions produce a persistent orange flame.

E Calcium ions produce a brick-red flame.

F Barium ions produce a green flame.

These different colours are also useful in producing different coloured fireworks.

6 Make a list of all of the flame colours for the metals listed above.

7 Draw a series of diagrams showing how a sample of water could be analysed to show what metal ions are present. Add captions to each of your diagrams to explain what is happening.

Detecting positive ions

By the end of this topic you should be able to:

- distinguish between some metal ions by their reaction with sodium hydroxide solution
- test for ammonium ions using sodium hydroxide solution.

Using the results of chemical tests

Flame tests cannot always be used to identify metal ions. However, we can use the fact that many metals form insoluble hydroxides when they are reacted with **sodium hydroxide** (NaOH) solution. For example, magnesium chloride reacts with sodium hydroxide to form insoluble magnesium hydroxide and sodium chloride:

$$MgCl_2(aq) + 2NaOH(aq) \longrightarrow Mg(OH)_2(s) + 2NaCl(aq)$$

A This could contain magnesium, calcium or aluminium ions.

Calcium, magnesium and aluminium ions all form white solid **precipitates** when they are reacted with sodium hydroxide solution. So if an unknown solution forms a white precipitate with sodium hydroxide solution, we need to test whether it contains magnesium, calcium or aluminium ions. We can distinguish the aluminium ions from the other two if more sodium hydroxide solution is added, because the white precipitate dissolves again. This doesn't happen for magnesium or calcium. Magnesium and calcium ions can be distinguished by using a flame test.

1 Write a word equation for the reaction between aluminium nitrate solution and sodium hydroxide solution.

2 Would anything happen if you mixed solutions of potassium chloride and sodium hydroxide? Explain your answer.

3 What flame colours do you get with magnesium and calcium ions?

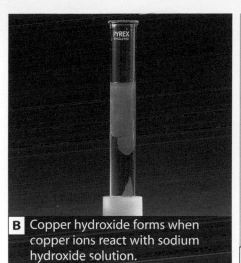

B Copper hydroxide forms when copper ions react with sodium hydroxide solution.

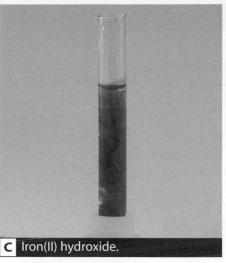

C Iron(II) hydroxide.

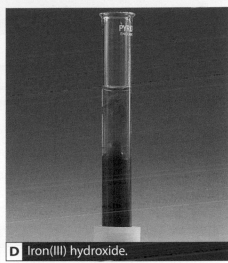

D Iron(III) hydroxide.

Other metal ions form coloured precipitates with sodium hydroxide solution. If sodium hydroxide solution is added to a solution containing copper ions, for example copper sulfate, a blue precipitate of copper hydroxide is formed. If a solution of sodium hydroxide and a solution containing iron(II) (Fe^{2+}) ions are mixed, a green precipitate of iron(II) hydroxide is formed. Iron(III) (Fe^{3+}) ions form a reddish-brown precipitate.

4 Write a balanced symbol equation showing the formation of
  a iron(II) hydroxide ($Fe(OH)_2$) from iron(II) chloride ($FeCl_2$) and sodium hydroxide solution
  b iron(III) hydroxide ($Fe(OH)_3$) from iron(III) chloride ($FeCl_3$) and sodium hydroxide solution.

Sodium hydroxide solution can also be used to detect the presence of ammonium ions (NH_4^+). Ammonium ions react with sodium hydroxide solution to form ammonia gas, which is driven off when the mixture is gently heated. As ammonia gas is alkaline, it turns damp red litmus paper blue and can be easily identified.

ammonium chloride + sodium hydroxide ⟶ ammonia + sodium chloride + water
$NH_4Cl(aq)$ + $NaOH(aq)$ ⟶ $NH_3(g)$ + $NaCl(aq)$ + $H_2O(l)$

5 Write a word equation for the reaction between ammonium nitrate and sodium hydroxide solution.

6 Copy and complete this table showing the reaction of sodium hydroxide with different positive ions:

Ion present	Observation
Aluminium	
Ammonium	
Calcium	
Copper	
Iron(II)	
Iron(III)	
Magnesium	

Looking at carbonates

By the end of this topic you should be able to:

- describe how carbonates react with acids to form carbon dioxide
- describe how carbon dioxide turns limewater milky
- describe how zinc carbonate and copper carbonate decompose when they are heated, and how they can be identified.

Using the results of chemical tests

You have seen that many metal ions can be identified either by the colour of their flame or by their reaction with sodium hydroxide solution.

Although there are many different metal ions, there are far fewer non-metal ions. Some of the most important are shown in Table A.

Carbonates are very easy to distinguish from other types of compounds. If you react a carbonate with a dilute acid, carbon dioxide is formed. You can test for this by bubbling the gas through limewater and seeing if it turns milky.

Ion	Formula
Carbonate	CO_3^{2-}
Chloride	Cl^-
Nitrate	NO_3^-
Sulfate	SO_4^{2-}

A Examples of non-metal ions.

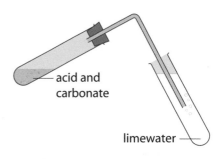

acid and carbonate

limewater

B Testing for carbonates.

For example, sodium carbonate reacts with hydrochloric acid to form sodium chloride, carbon dioxide and water:

$$Na_2CO_3(aq) + 2HCl(aq) \rightarrow 2NaCl(aq) + CO_2(g) + H_2O(l)$$

Limewater contains calcium hydroxide solution. When carbon dioxide is bubbled through limewater it turns milky, since the carbon dioxide reacts with the calcium hydroxide solution to form insoluble calcium carbonate and water:

$$Ca(OH)_2(aq) + CO_2(g) \rightarrow CaCO_3(s) + H_2O(l)$$

1 Write down the reaction between calcium carbonate and hydrochloric acid as:
  a a word equation
  b a balanced symbol equation.

2 Explain why acids can be used to remove limescale from kettles.

3 Where might we come across calcium hydrogencarbonate in our everyday lives?

If more carbon dioxide solution is bubbled through the calcium carbonate formed, soluble calcium hydrogencarbonate is formed and the mixture goes clear again:

$$CaCO_3(s) + CO_2(g) + H_2O(l) \rightarrow Ca(HCO_3)_2(aq)$$

Many carbonates decompose when heated, forming the metal oxide and carbon dioxide. For example, calcium carbonate decomposes to form calcium oxide and carbon dioxide:

$$CaCO_3(s) \rightarrow CaO(s) + CO_2(g)$$

When copper carbonate is heated, it decomposes to form copper oxide. This reaction has a very distinctive colour change as copper carbonate is green and copper oxide is black:

$$CuCO_3(s) \rightarrow CuO(s) + CO_2(g)$$

The decomposition of zinc carbonate also shows a characteristic colour change. Zinc carbonate is white, as is zinc oxide. However, when zinc oxide is hot it is yellow. We therefore see the mix turn from white to yellow to white again when it is cooled.

$$ZnCO_3(s) \rightarrow ZnO(s) + CO_2(g)$$

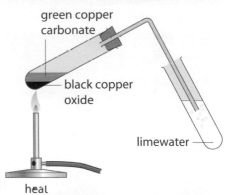

C The black copper oxide being formed can be seen in the bottom of the test tube.

D Zinc oxide is the only compound that changes colour in this way when heated.

4 Write a balanced symbol equation for the decomposition of iron(II) carbonate ($FeCO_3$).

5 How could you distinguish between white calcium carbonate and zinc carbonate?

6 Is the change of colour of zinc oxide when heated a physical or a chemical change?

7 Draw a flow chart showing all the possible reactions involving calcium carbonate. Include the effect of heat and its reactions with acids and carbon dioxide solution.

Testing for other non-metal ions

By the end of this topic you should be able to:

- describe how to test for halide ions using silver nitrate solution
- describe how to test for sulfate ions using barium chloride solution
- describe how to test for nitrate ions using aluminium powder and sodium hydroxide solution.

Using the results of chemical tests

Testing for halides

The **halides** are the ions formed by the Group 7 halogens. Fluorine forms fluoride ions (F^-), chlorine forms chloride ions (Cl^-), bromine forms bromide ions (Br^-) and iodine forms iodide ions (I^-). These can be distinguished from one another by adding silver nitrate solution ($AgNO_3$) to a solution of the halide ions. Fluoride ions do not react with silver nitrate solution, but if chloride ions are present a white precipitate of silver chloride forms. Bromide ions produce a cream precipitate of silver bromide. Iodide ions produce a yellow precipitate of silver iodide.

AgCl   AgBr   AgI

A How to distinguish between halide ions.

B Some people learn these colours by remembering that milk is used to make cream, which is then converted into butter.

For example:

silver nitrate + sodium bromide → silver bromide + sodium nitrate
$$AgNO_3(aq) + NaBr(aq) \rightarrow AgBr(s) + NaNO_3(aq)$$

1 What would you see if you added silver nitrate solution to potassium iodide solution?

2 What might be a problem if you added silver nitrate solution to blue copper chloride solution?

Testing for sulfates

A solution of a **sulfate** reacts with a solution of barium chloride to form a white insoluble precipitate of barium sulfate. For example:

sodium sulfate + barium chloride → barium sulfate + sodium chloride

$$Na_2SO_4(aq) + BaCl_2(aq) \rightarrow BaSO_4(s) + 2NaCl(aq)$$

barium chloride solution

sodium sulfate solution

barium sulfate precipitate

C Testing for sulfate ions.

3 What would you see if barium chloride ($BaCl_2$) solution was added to potassium sulfate (K_2SO_4) solution?

4 Write a balanced symbol equation for this reaction.

5 What do the tests for halide ions and sulfate ions have in common?

Testing for nitrates

To test for **nitrate** ions, sodium hydroxide solution is gently warmed with a solution containing the unknown ions. Aluminium powder is then added. The aluminium reduces the nitrate ions to ammonia, which is detected using damp red litmus paper.

6 What other ion reacts with just sodium hydroxide solution to form ammonia?

7 Would anything happen if sodium hydroxide solution was added to potassium chloride?

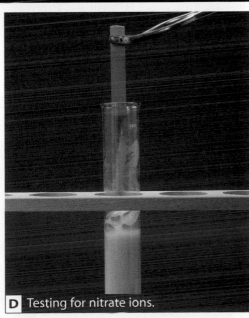

D Testing for nitrate ions.

8 Describe how you would find out which non-metal ions are in a colourless solution labelled Q.

P

P

D

P

P

83

Testing for acidity

By the end of this topic you should be able to:

- explain that water must be present for a substance to act as an acid or an alkali
- explain that acids produce hydrated hydrogen ions in aqueous solution, and alkalis produce hydroxide ions in solution
- explain the difference between strong and weak acids and alkalis, giving examples of each

H

- evaluate the contributions of Arrhenius, Brønsted and Lowry to our understanding of acid–base behaviour
- define acids as proton donors, and bases as proton acceptors.

Water companies also need to know the acidity of their water. Acids and alkalis need water to work. This can be shown by dissolving citric acid first in water and then in dry propanone. The aqueous solution has typical acidic properties but the solution in propanone does not.

1 Give three typical properties of acids.

When acidic compounds are added to water they **ionise**, which means that they split up and form ions. Hydrochloric acid ionises to form hydrogen ions and chloride ions:

$$HCl(aq) \rightarrow H^+(aq) + Cl^-(aq)$$

A hydrogen ion is the same as a proton. The proton reacts with water molecules and becomes **hydrated**, and is represented as $H^+(aq)$.

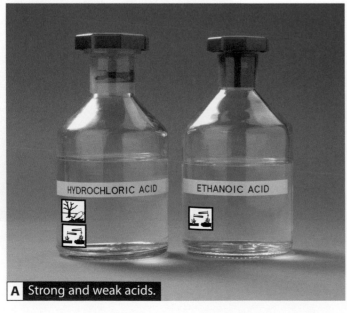

A Strong and weak acids.

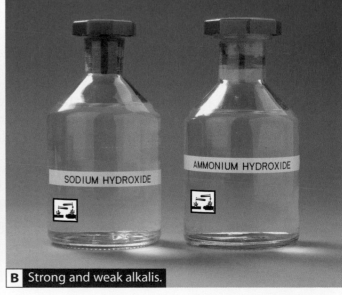

B Strong and weak alkalis.

Acids that totally ionise in water are called strong acids, while those that only partially ionise are called weak acids. Hydrochloric, nitric and sulfuric acids are all strong acids. Ethanoic, citric and carbonic acids are all weak acids. Similarly, strong alkalis like sodium hydroxide and potassium hydroxide completely ionise in water, while weak alkalis like ammonium hydroxide only partially ionise in water.

2 Write definitions for the following: hydrogen ion, strong acid, weak acid, strong alkali, weak alkali.

H

Changing ideas of acidity

For hundreds of years, scientists knew that acids tasted sour and had some effect on natural indicators like the colour from red cabbage. In 1884 a young chemist called Arrhenius first defined an acid scientifically. He suggested that acids split up in water to form hydrogen ions, and bases produced hydroxide ions in water.

However, Arrhenius's theory referred only to reactions in water, and his ideas were rejected at first by other scientists who didn't believe that molecules could ionise. More data eventually supported his ideas and Arrhenius was finally given credit for his theory.

The problem of acid–base reactions occurring without the presence of water was solved in 1923 by two chemists called Brønsted and Lowry. Working independently, they both came up with the following general definitions:

Acids are **proton donors**.
Bases are **proton acceptors**.

3 Why did Arrhenius's theory take so long to be accepted?

4 Why do you think that the Brønsted–Lowry theory was more readily accepted by scientists in 1923?

5 Ammonia and hydrogen chloride react together to form ammonium chloride:
$NH_3(g) + HCl(g) \rightarrow NH_4Cl(s)$
a Why does this not fit with Arrhenius's theory?
b Why does this fit with the Brønsted–Lowry theory?

6 Write an encyclopedia entry called 'Acids and alkalis'.

Detecting organic chemicals

By the end of this topic you should be able to:

- describe how organic compounds burn or char in air
- explain that unsaturated organic compounds containing a double bond decolourise bromine water
- find the empirical formula of an organic compound from the masses of the products formed when a known mass of the compound is burned.

Organic chemistry is the chemistry of carbon and its compounds. Carbon is able to form strong covalent bonds with itself and some other elements. It can also form long chains and rings, resulting in at least seven million different **organic compounds**. The presence of carbon causes all organic compounds to burn or char when heated in air.

1 Name one compound containing carbon that does not char when heated in air. (*Hint:* Look at Topic C3.10)

2 Do you consider the definition of organic chemistry given above to be valid?

Organic chemicals can be divided into different groups. For example, hydrocarbons are divided into **saturated** alkanes and **unsaturated** alkenes which contain carbon–carbon double bonds. We can distinguish between these because of the double bond in alkenes. Alkenes decolourise bromine water, while alkanes do not.

A Bread contains organic compounds.

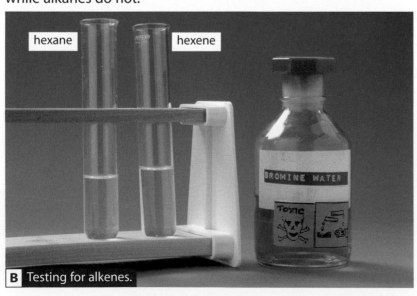

hexane   hexene

BROMINE WATER

Toxic

B Testing for alkenes.

3 How would you use bromine water to differentiate between hexane and hexene?

H The **empirical formula** of a compound shows the simplest ratio of the number of atoms in a molecule of that compound. For example, the empirical formula of ethane (C_2H_6) is CH_3, and that of glucose ($C_6H_{12}O_6$) is CH_2O.

4 What is the empirical formula of:
   a hexane, C_6H_{14}?
   b benzene, C_6H_6?

The empirical formula of a compound is found by a process called combustion analysis. A sample of the compound is taken, its mass is measured accurately, and the sample is then burned in excess oxygen. The carbon in the compound turns into carbon dioxide and the hydrogen burns to form water. The mass of both products is measured.

One mole of carbon dioxide has a mass of 44 g of which 12 g is carbon, so $^{12}/_{44}$ of the mass of carbon dioxide formed is the mass of the carbon present.

One mole of water has a mass of 18 g of which 2 g is hydrogen, so $^{2}/_{18}$ of the mass of water formed is the mass of the hydrogen present.

The masses of carbon and hydrogen are used to calculate the moles of each element and hence the empirical formula.

Suppose 0.29 g of a hydrocarbon is burned to form 0.88 g of carbon dioxide and 0.45 g of water.

0.88 g of carbon dioxide contains $0.88 \times {}^{12}/_{44} = 0.24$ g of carbon

0.45 g of water contains $0.45 \times {}^{2}/_{18} = 0.05$ g of hydrogen

0.24 g of carbon is $^{0.24}/_{12} = 0.02$ moles of carbon

0.05 g of hydrogen is $^{0.05}/_{1} = 0.05$ moles of hydrogen

The simplest ratio of carbon to hydrogen is $0.02 : 0.05 = 2 : 5$, so the empirical formula is C_2H_5.

---

5 In an experiment, 0.112 g of a hydrocarbon burned in excess oxygen to produce 0.352 g of carbon dioxide and 0.144 g of water. Calculate its empirical formula.

6 Explain why it is important to detect organic compounds in water.

By the end of this topic you should be able to:

- describe how the development of modern instrumental methods has been aided by the rapid progress in technology
- appreciate that instrumental methods are accurate, sensitive and rapid
- appreciate that instrumental methods are particularly useful when the amount of sample is very small.

Using instruments to analyse substances

A Analysing water.

The tests that you have carried out to detect which ions are present in aqueous solution all rely on quite large amounts of each ion being present. However, water companies must also check that there are only tiny amounts of some ions that are poisonous. Table B shows the mean average values for some ions found in a series of water samples.

A microgram is 1/1 000 000 (one millionth) of a gram, or 0.000 001 g.

Concentrations are also sometimes expressed as parts per million (ppm). Therefore 1 microgram of arsenic in 1 dm³ (one litre) of water is 0.000 001 g in 1 dm³ of water. 1 dm³ of water weighs 1000 g, so the concentration of arsenic is 0.001 ppm.

Ion	Mean average concentration (micrograms/dm³ of water)
Aluminium	<5.0
Arsenic	<1.0
Lead	<1.0
Mercury	<0.10
Nitrate	21.0

B Concentrations of some harmful ions in water.

1 What is the concentration in ppm of aluminium ions in this sample?

2 Where do the nitrate ions come from?

Analysts in a water company therefore need to use very sensitive instruments to detect quantities of ions to this accuracy. Many years ago this was often done by titration, but this was slow and not very accurate. Nowadays, modern instruments that depend on the use of electronics and computers are used. The sample of water is placed in one part of a machine, and a print-out showing the concentration of several different ions is produced quickly.

C Checking for the absence of poisonous chemicals.

A variety of instrumental methods can be used to detect and identify both elements and compounds. These instrumental methods are accurate, sensitive and rapid. They are particularly useful when the amount of a sample is very small. They can also detect large organic molecules such as pesticides, so that we can be certain that the water we drink is safe. The presence of radioactive particles can also be determined. However, these instruments are expensive and the people using them have to be trained to a high level.

Amounts of bacteria are still estimated by growing the bacteria in a nutrient and counting the amount produced in a certain time. This is particularly important in checking that there is no sewage in a water sample.

3 Give three advantages of using modern instrumental methods for analysing water samples.

4 Give two disadvantages of this method of analysis.

5 How might radioactive particles get into water?

6 Why do we need to find out how many bacteria are present in a sample of water?

7 Write a leaflet aimed at consumers which explains how water samples are analysed.

Instrumental analysis

H **_By the end of this topic you should be able to:_**

- describe how some instrumental methods are suited to identifying elements
- describe how other instrumental methods are suited to identifying compounds
- describe how some methods can be adapted for identifying both elements and compounds.

Specific instruments for specific purposes

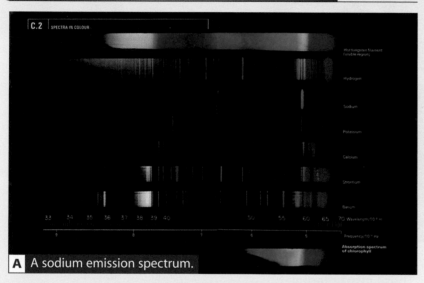

A A sodium emission spectrum.

Some instrumental methods are suitable for identifying elements. **Atomic spectrometers** are expensive machines which analyse the energy (usually light) absorbed or given out by a sample. A solution of the sample is injected into a flame. As in a flame test, this causes light to be emitted. This light is broken up into its component colours, forming a **line emission spectrum**. Each element has its own specific line emission spectrum. The various frequencies of these lines are measured automatically and a computer compares them with its database to get the correct match. This method is very accurate, being used extensively in analysing water. For example, it can detect 0.01 micrograms of lead in 1 dm^3 of water. It is also used in the steel industry, where it can analyse precisely the amounts of trace elements present in steel to control its quality.

1 **a** What process have you carried out which is similar to the action of an atomic spectrometer?
  b Why did you use it?

2 Give two uses of atomic spectrometry.

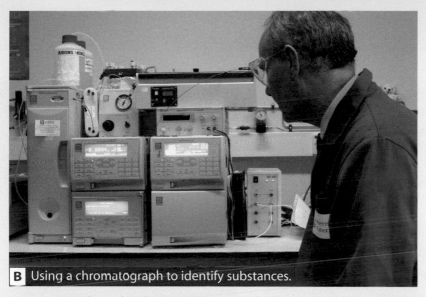

B Using a chromatograph to identify substances.

Instrumental methods suited to identifying compounds include the following.

- **Infrared spectroscopy.** This is used to detect specific bonds in organic compounds, such as pesticide residues in water.
- **Ultraviolet spectroscopy.** This is used to analyse levels of nitrates and phosphates in water.
- **Nuclear magnetic resonance spectroscopy.** This is also used to detect some organic molecules.
- **Gas–liquid chromatography.** Unlike paper chromatography that is used, for example, to separate solid colours, gas–liquid chromatography separates gases by passing them through a long column containing silicon dioxide or aluminium oxide. The gases separate and are identified by comparison with the distances moved by known substances.

3 Which of the methods listed above are used for:
   a organic compounds?
   b analysing water?
   Explain your answers.

Perhaps the most useful instrument is the **mass spectrometer**. This can be used for both elements and compounds. It can also measure the relative formula mass of the sample, so it can be used to analyse the sample or identify elements. The sample is vapourised and ionised, which breaks up the molecules into smaller fragments. These fragments are detected and the masses of the fragments are used to detect what is in the sample.

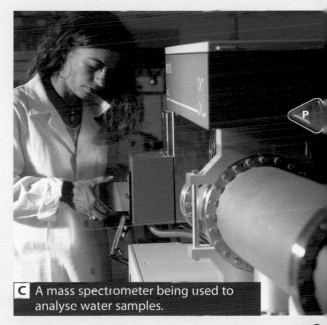

C A mass spectrometer being used to analyse water samples.

4 Isotopes are atoms of the same element – they have the same atomic number but different masses. How could a mass spectrometer be useful in finding out how many isotopes an element has?

5 List two advantages that a mass spectrometer has over the other instrumental methods described.

6 Write an article for the school science magazine explaining the importance of modern instrumental techniques in analysing water.

Investigative Skills Assessment

Langhit and Hannah were given samples of water from different parts of the country. These were labelled A–D. They used the apparatus shown in the diagram to find out whether the samples contained hard or soft water. They then boiled each sample and found out how much soap solution was needed to make a lather. Their results are shown in the table. Each experiment was repeated.

| Sample | Volume of soap needed to make a lather (cm³) | | | |
| | With unboiled water | | With boiled water | |
	First attempt	Second attempt	First attempt	Second attempt
A	23.5	24.1	24.2	23.8
B	1.2	1.4	1.5	1.1
C	21.9	22.6	1.7	1.2
D	26.7	27.1	13.9	13.6

1 List the four types of water in order of decreasing hardness. *(1 mark)*

2 Calculate the average volumes of soap used for each water sample A–D, both unboiled and boiled. Name each of the eight average volumes clearly. *(2 marks)*

3 a Which water was permanently hard? *(1 mark)*
   b Which water was temporarily hard? *(1 mark)*
   c Which water was soft? *(1 mark)*
   d Which water was a mixture of temporarily hard water and permanently hard water? *(1 mark)*

4 What could have been used as a control? *(1 mark)*

5 What should Langhit and Hannah have done to make their results more accurate? *(1 mark)*

6 Why are their results not very consistent? *(1 mark)*

7 How could they check the reliability of their results? *(1 mark)*

8 What further controls could have been put in place to make their results more valid? *(2 marks)*

9 Would better results have been obtained if the whole class's results had been pooled? Explain your answer. *(2 marks)*

10 Why should you not draw a line graph of these results? *(1 mark)*

11 How should these results be presented? *(1 mark)*

12 ✎ Hard water forms a scum with soap. How could you try to compare the amount of scum formed with each water sample? *(2 marks)*

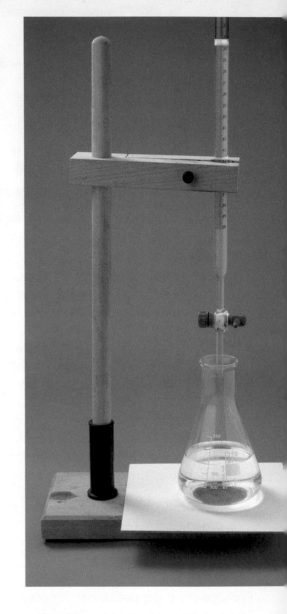

Driving chemistry further

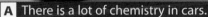

A There is a lot of chemistry in cars.

There is a lot of chemistry involved in a car. Many different materials are used to make the car. The body and engine are made from different metals and alloys. Some of these metals are transition metals, which are a block of elements in the Periodic Table. Cars are powered by burning fuels, engine parts are lubricated by oil, and chemical reactions take place in the battery to power the electrics. Car batteries contain sulfuric acid and in this unit you will learn how to perform titrations to calculate the concentration of acids. Most cars use petrol or diesel as a fuel because these fuels release a lot of heat energy when they burn. In this unit you will look at all these different ways in which chemistry is used in cars.

By the end of this unit you should be able to:

- describe how elements are arranged in the Periodic Table and link the position of an element in the Periodic Table to its properties
- describe the chemical and physical properties of the elements in Group 1, Group 7 and the transition metals
- describe how the Periodic Table developed from early ideas about the elements
- perform mole calculations for reactions in solution
- perform an acid–alkali titration, choosing a suitable indicator
- calculate the energy change in a reaction using bond energies
- perform experiments to calculate the energy change for a chemical reaction in solution or when a fuel or food is burned
- evaluate issues surrounding the use of fuels
- describe which foods contain most energy and how this is linked to obesity.

1 List as many ways as you can in which chemistry is used in cars.

2 List all the ways you can think of in which vehicles have changed the way we live. Include both positive and negative ways in your list.

The Periodic Table

Elements cannot be broken down into simpler substances. They contain just one type of atom. For example, all the atoms in the element carbon are carbon atoms. All the elements are listed in the **Periodic Table**.

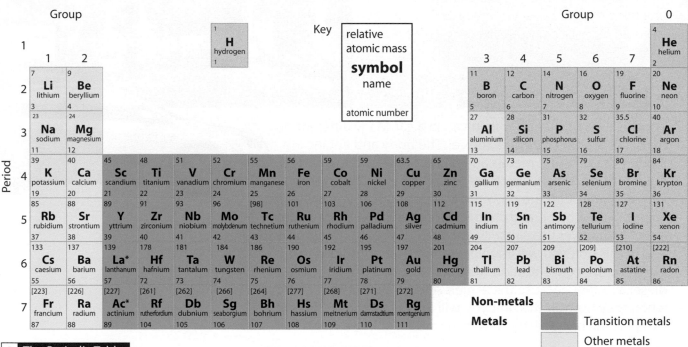

A The Periodic Table.

In the Periodic Table, the elements are listed in order of atomic number. The **atomic number** (or **proton number**) of an atom is the number of protons it contains.

Elements are classified as either metals or non-metals. There is a dividing line between metals and non-metals. Over three-quarters of the elements are metals. The non-metals are found in the top right-hand corner of the table.

The vertical columns are called **groups**. The groups are commonly numbered 1, 2, 3, 4, 5, 6, 7 and 0. The horizontal rows are called **periods**. There is a block of elements between Group 2 and Group 3 called the **transition metals**. Some groups have special names:

Group 1 – the alkali metals
Group 7 – the halogens
Group 0 – the noble gases.

1 What is the Periodic Table?

2 How are the elements arranged in the Periodic Table?

3 Use the Periodic Table to help you find the symbol of
   a an element in Group 6
   b a transition metal
   c the element in Group 3, Period 3
   d a metal in Group 4
   e a non-metal in Group 5.

There is a link between the position of an element in the Periodic Table and its electronic structure. The number of electrons in the outer energy level (shell) of an atom is the same as the group number. For example, all the elements in Group 1 have one electron in their outer energy level (e.g. lithium = 2,1; sodium = 2,8,1; potassium = 2,8,8,1), while all the elements in Group 7 have seven electrons in their outer energy level (e.g. fluorine = 2,7; chlorine = 2,8,7).

Elements in the same group of the Periodic Table have similar chemical properties. For example, all the elements in Group 1 are metals that react with water, and all the elements in Group 0 are gases that are very unreactive. The reason for this is that elements in the same group have the same number of electrons in their outer energy level. The table is called the Periodic Table because similar properties occur at regular intervals.

The period number is equal to the number of energy levels that contain electrons. For example, elements in Period 3 have three energy levels containing electrons (e.g. potassium = 2,8,1; chlorine = 2,8,7).

4 An element has two electrons in its outer energy level. Which group of the Periodic Table is it in?

5 Explain why elements in the same group have similar chemical properties.

6 An element has the electronic structure 2,8,3.
   a Which group in the Periodic Table is the element in?
   b Which period in the Periodic Table is the element in?
   c What is the atomic number of the element?

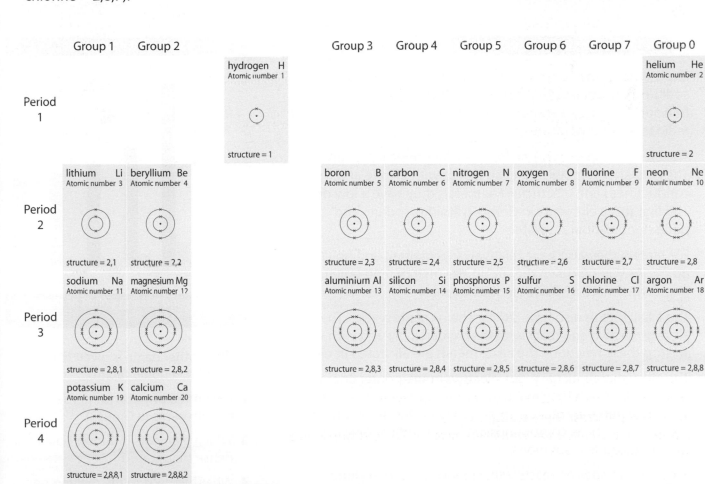

B Electronic structure of the first 20 elements.

Group 1 – the alkali metals

By the end of this topic you should be able to:

H
- describe the chemical and physical properties of the alkali metals
- explain the trend in reactivity of the alkali metals.

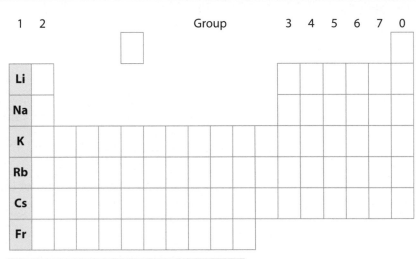

A   The alkali metals in the Periodic Table.

B   Sodium being cut with a knife.

The elements in Group 1 of the Periodic Table are lithium (Li), sodium (Na), potassium (K), rubidium (Rb), caesium (Cs) and francium (Fr). They are known as the **alkali metals**. Francium is radioactive and very rare.

The elements in Group 1 all have similar physical properties. They are all soft metals that can be cut with a knife and conduct heat and electricity. For metals they have a low density. The first three elements in Group 1, lithium, sodium and potassium, all float on water.

For metals, they also have relatively low melting and boiling points. As you go down the group, the melting and boiling points get lower, as shown in the bar chart.

The alkali metals also have similar chemical properties. They are all very reactive and react with the oxygen in air and with water. To stop these reactions, the alkali metals are all stored in oil.

The alkali metals all have one electron in their outer energy level (shell). When they react, they lose this electron and form 1+ ions. When they react with non-metals, they form ionic compounds. These compounds are white and dissolve in water to form colourless solutions.

For example, sodium reacts with chlorine to form sodium chloride, which is a white ionic compound containing Na^+ ions. Sodium chloride dissolves in water to form a colourless solution.

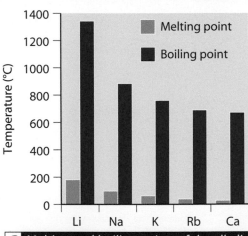

C   Melting and boiling points of the alkali metals.

1 What other name is given to Group 1 in the Periodic Table?

2 Give three physical properties of all the elements in Group 1.

3 Which elements in Group 1 are less dense than water?

4 What happens to the melting points as you go down Group 1?

5 Potassium reacts with bromine.
  a Name the compound formed.
  b What type of bonding does this compound have?
  c Give the formula and charge of the potassium ion in this compound.
  d What colour is this compound?
  e What will happen if this compound is added to water?

When the alkali metals react with water, they form a metal hydroxide and hydrogen. The metal hydroxides dissolve in water, making an alkaline solution:

  metal + water ⟶ metal hydroxide + hydrogen

For example:

  sodium + water ⟶ sodium hydroxide + hydrogen
  $2Na$ + $2H_2O$ ⟶ $2NaOH$ + H_2

D Sodium reacts with chlorine to make sodium chloride.

E Sodium reacting with water.   Caesium reacting with water.

The reactions get more and more vigorous as you go down the group. This is because the alkali metals become more reactive as you go down the group.

H When the alkali metals react, the electron in the outer energy level (shell) is lost. As you go down the group, the atoms get bigger, so the outer electron is further from the nucleus. This means that the attraction from the nucleus to the outer electron is weaker and so the electron is easier to lose. This is why the alkali metals become more reactive as you go down the group.

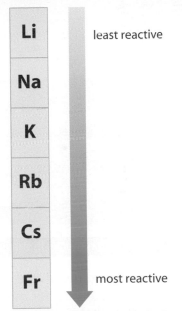

F Trend in reactivity of the alkali metals.

Li   least reactive
Na
K
Rb
Cs
Fr   most reactive

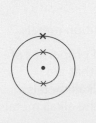

  lithium (2,1)   sodium (2,8,1)   potassium (2,8,8,1)

G As the atoms get bigger, the outer shell electron is further from the nucleus.

6 a Write a word equation for the reaction of lithium with water.
  b Explain why the solution formed is alkaline.
  c Why is the reaction of lithium with water less vigorous than that of sodium?

7 Write a fact card for the elements in Group 1. Include ten key facts.

Transition metals

> **By the end of this topic you should be able to:**
> - describe the physical and chemical properties of the transition metals and compare them to the alkali metals
> - describe special properties of the transition metals
> - explain why the transition metals have special properties.

The transition metals are a block of elements between Group 2 and Group 3 in the Periodic Table. Many common metals including iron, copper, nickel, silver, gold and platinum are transition metals.

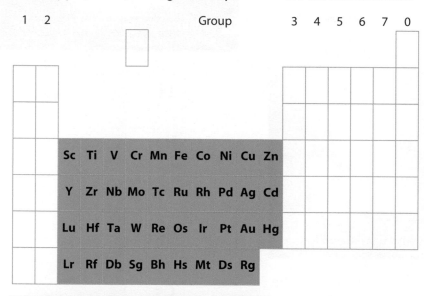

A The transition metals in the Periodic Table.

B Many transition metals are used in cars.

Many transition metals are used to make cars. For example, iron is used to make steel for the body, platinum and palladium are used in the catalytic converter, and chromium and nickel are used in many alloys for engine parts.

The transition metals all have similar physical properties. They are hard and strong with high melting and boiling points, they have high densities, and they conduct heat and electricity.

C Gold does not react with water or oxygen.

They also have similar chemical properties. They react slowly, if at all, with water and oxygen. For example, iron reacts with oxygen and water, only very slowly, when it rusts. Other transition metals, such as gold, do not react at all with water or oxygen.

Compared to Group 1 metals, the transition metals:
- have higher melting points (except mercury which is a liquid at room temperature)
- have higher densities
- are stronger and harder
- are much less reactive.

1 Name three transition metals.

2 Give two physical properties of transition metals that are
   a similar to the alkali metals
   b different from the alkali metals.

3 a Describe how transition metals react with water and oxygen.
   b How does this compare to the alkali metals?

Transition metals also have some special properties that other metals do not have. They are useful as catalysts. A **catalyst** is a substance that speeds up a chemical reaction without being used up itself. Some important examples are shown in Table D.

Process	Equation	Catalyst
Making margarine	vegetable oils + hydrogen ⟶ margarine	nickel
Making ammonia	hydrogen + nitrogen ⟶ ammonia	iron
Catalytic converters	carbon monoxide + nitrogen monoxide ⟶ carbon dioxide + nitrogen	platinum

D Some industrial uses of transition metal catalysts.

Compounds containing transition metals are usually coloured. For example, many pottery glazes contain transition metal compounds. Some statues and roofs are made of copper, which reacts with substances in the air to produce an attractive green compound containing copper. Many gemstones, including rubies, are coloured due to transition metal compounds.

Transition metals can also form ions with different charges. For example, copper can form Cu^+ and Cu^{2+} ions, and iron can form Fe^{2+} and Fe^{3+} ions.

4 Give three special properties of transition metals compared to other metals.

H Transition metals have these special properties due to their electronic structure. Across each row of transition metals, an inner energy level (shell) of electrons is being filled. For example, in the first row of the transition metals, the electrons fill the third energy level, even though there are already some electrons in the fourth energy level. The third energy level holds 18 electrons, but after the first eight electrons have entered the energy level, the next two electrons enter the fourth energy level, before the next 10 electrons fill up the third energy level. The electronic structure of iron is 2,8,14,2 and that of nickel is 2,8,16,2.

5 The atomic number of titanium is 22. Give the electronic structure of titanium.

6 Explain why transition metals have special properties compared to other metals.

7 Potassium and cobalt are both in Period 3 of the Periodic Table. Potassium is an alkali metal. Cobalt is a transition metal. Make a list of similarities and differences between potassium and cobalt.

E The Statue of Liberty is green due to a compound containing copper.

F Rubies are red due to a chromium compound.

Group 7 – the halogens

By the end of this topic you should be able to:

- describe the chemical and physical properties of the halogens

H
- explain the trend in reactivity of the halogens.

The elements in Group 7 of the Periodic Table are fluorine (F), chlorine (Cl), bromine (Br), iodine (I) and astatine (At). They are known as the **halogens**. Astatine is radioactive and very rare.

The elements in Group 7 all have similar physical properties. They are all non-metals with coloured vapours. They do not conduct heat or electricity. They are all made of molecules which contain two atoms (diatomic molecules). For example, chlorine molecules have the formula Cl_2. They all have low melting and boiling points because there are weak forces between the molecules. As you go down the group, the melting and boiling points get higher (see Table B).

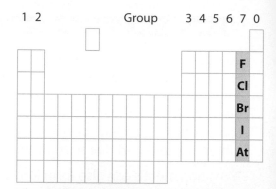

A The halogens in the Periodic Table.

Property	Element			
	Fluorine	**Chlorine**	**Bromine**	**Iodine**
Formula of molecules	F_2	Cl_2	Br_2	I_2
Melting point (°C)	−220	−101	−7	114
Boiling point (°C)	−188	−34	59	184
Appearance at room temperature	pale yellow gas	pale green gas	orange liquid	grey solid
Photo				
Colour of vapour	yellow	green	orange	purple

B Properties of the halogens.

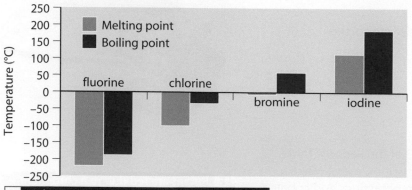

C Melting and boiling points of the halogens.

1 What other name is given to Group 7 in the Periodic Table?

2 Give three physical properties of all the elements in Group 7.

3 What happens to the boiling points as you go down Group 7?

The halogens also have similar chemical properties. This is because all the halogen atoms have seven electrons in their outer energy level (shell).

The halogens all react with metals to form ionic compounds containing halide ions. Electrons are transferred from the metal atoms to the halogen atoms, forming halide ions with 1– electric charges. For example, chlorine reacts with the metal sodium to form the ionic compound sodium chloride, which contains chloride ions (Cl^-). The halide ions are fluoride ions (F^-), chloride ions (Cl^-), bromide ions (Br^-) and iodide ions (I^-).

The halogens all react with non-metals to form molecular compounds containing covalent bonds. Electrons are shared between the atoms. For example, chlorine reacts with the non-metal hydrogen to form the molecular compound hydrogen chloride.

The halogens become less reactive as you go down the group.

H When the halogens react, the halogen atoms gain one electron. As you go down the group, the atoms get bigger, so the electron gained is further from the nucleus. This means that the attraction from the nucleus to the electron being gained is weaker and so the electron is harder to gain. This explains why the halogens become less reactive as you go down the group.

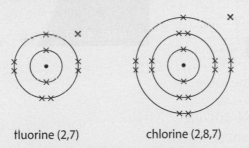

fluorine (2,7)   chlorine (2,8,7)

E As the atoms get bigger, the electron gained is further from the nucleus.

5 a Which is more reactive, bromine or iodine?
   b Explain why.

A more reactive halogen will displace a less reactive halogen from a compound in a **displacement reaction**. For example, chlorine will displace bromine from a solution of potassium bromide because chlorine is more reactive than bromine.

chlorine + potassium bromide → potassium chloride + bromine
Cl_2 + $2KBr$ → $2KCl$ + Br_2

6 Write a word equation for the following reactions, or write *no reaction* if nothing happens:
   a iodine + sodium chloride
   b fluorine + potassium chloride
   c bromine + sodium iodide.

4 What type of compound is formed when
   a chlorine reacts with magnesium?
   b fluorine reacts with nitrogen?
   c bromine reacts with calcium?

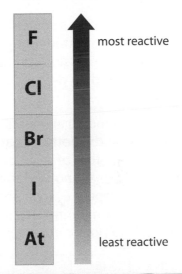

most reactive

least reactive

D Trend in reactivity of the halogens.

7 Write a fact card for the elements in Group 7. Include ten key facts.

Development of the Periodic Table

By the end of this topic you should be able to:

- describe the development of the Periodic Table, including the work by Newlands and Mendeleev.

In the early 1800s, about 30 elements were known. Several chemists had spotted that groups of elements, such as lithium, sodium and potassium, had similar properties. However, no one had found an overall pattern in the behaviour of the elements.

In 1864, around 50 elements were known. The British chemist John Newlands spotted a pattern when he arranged these elements in order of atomic mass, as in Table A which shows his first four rows. He noticed that the properties of the elements seemed to repeat every eighth element. He called this the 'law of octaves', comparing it to musical scales. For example, lithium, sodium and potassium are in the same column.

John Newlands.

H	Li	Be	B	C	N	O
F	Na	Mg	Al	Si	P	S
Cl	K	Ca	Cr	Ti	Mn	Fe
Co, Ni	Cu	Zn	Y	In	As	Se

A The first four rows of Newlands' table, the 'law of octaves'.

Newlands' ideas were not accepted at the time, since the table did not work after calcium. For example, copper, which is very unreactive, was in the same group as the highly reactive lithium, sodium and potassium. The metals cobalt and nickel, whose atomic masses are very similar, had to share the same position in the group containing the gases hydrogen, fluorine and chlorine.

1 a In what order did John Newlands arrange the elements?
  b What did he discover when he arranged them in this way?
  c Why were his ideas ignored at the time?

In 1869, Dmitri Mendeleev, a Russian chemist, devised a table which is the basis of the Periodic Table as we know it. Table B shows his first five periods. Although he did not know about Newlands' arrangement, his basic idea was the same. However, he realised that some elements had not yet been discovered and left gaps for them (shown by * in Table B).

	Group I	Group II	Group III	Group IV	Group V	Group VI	Group VII	Group VIII
Period 1	H							
Period 2	Li	Be	B	C	N	O	F	
Period 3	Na	Mg	Al	Si	P	S	Cl	
Period 4	K	Ca	*	Ti	V	Cr	Mn	Fe Co Ni
	Cu	Zn	*	*	As	Se	Br	
Period 5	Rb	Sr	Y	Zr	Nb	Mo	*	Ru Rh Pd
	Ag	Cd	In	Sn	Sb	Te	I	

B The first five periods of Mendeleev's table.

Mendeleev went further and used the patterns in his table to predict the properties of the elements he thought had yet to be discovered. Three of these elements were discovered in the next few years and his predictions were very accurate. Table C shows his predictions about the properties of the element between silicon and tin (he called it 'eka-silicon', Es). It also shows the actual properties of the element when it was discovered in 1886 (called germanium).

Property	'Eka-silicon' (Es)	Germanium (Ge)
Appearance	grey metal	grey-white metal
Melting point	over 800°C	947°C
Atomic mass	72	72.3
Density	5.5 g/cm^3	5.47 g/cm^3
Formula of oxide	EsO_2	GeO_2
Formula of chloride	$EsCl_4$	$GeCl_4$

C Predicted and actual properties of germanium.

Dmitri Mendeleev.

In devising his table, Mendeleev did not stick completely to the atomic mass order. For example, he swapped iodine (I) and tellurium (Te) round because iodine fitted better with fluorine, chlorine and bromine than tellurium did. Following the discovery of protons, neutrons and electrons in the early 20th century, we now know that the elements are placed in order of atomic number, not atomic mass. Mendeleev thought that the atomic masses of some elements had been measured inaccurately. He had actually placed the elements in order of atomic number, even though he did not know it.

Mendeleev's table was accepted because many of his remarkable predictions about undiscovered elements proved to be correct. His table has been modified as more elements, including the noble gases, have been discovered, but the modern table is based on Mendeleev's.

2 a What did Mendeleev do differently from Newlands?
b What convinced people that Mendeleev's table was useful?

3 a In what order did Mendeleev put the elements?
b Why did he not put the elements in strict atomic mass order?
c Why did he not know about atomic numbers?

4 Describe how Newlands and Mendeleev contributed to the modern Periodic Table.

Solution calculations

- calculate the chemical quantities for reactions in solution.

$$\text{concentration (mol/dm}^3) = \frac{\text{moles}}{\text{volume (dm}^3)}$$

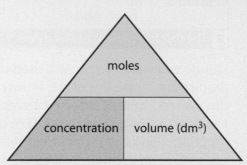

The concentration of a solution measures how much solute is dissolved in a solvent. This is usually measured in moles per cubic decimetre (mol/dm³), that is how many moles of solute are dissolved in one cubic decimetre (1 litre) of solution. A solution with a concentration of 0.100 mol/dm³ has 0.100 moles of solute dissolved per 1 dm³ of solution.

You need to be able to use the equation shown on the right. Often, the volume of a solution is given in cm³ and needs to be converted into dm³. There are 1000 cm³ in 1 dm³, so the volume in cm³ is divided by 1000 to give the volume in dm³.

Example 1
Calculate the concentration of a solution of sulfuric acid that contains 0.200 moles of sulfuric acid in 100 cm³.

concentration = $\frac{\text{number of moles}}{\text{volume (dm}^3)}$

= 0.200 / ($^{100}/_{1000}$)

= **2.0 mol/dm³**

Example 2
Calculate the number of moles of sodium hydroxide in 25 cm³ of 0.100 mol/dm³ sodium hydroxide solution.
number of moles = concentration × volume (dm³)
= 0.100 × ($^{25}/_{1000}$)

= **0.0025 moles**

Example 3
What volume of 0.500 mol/dm³ hydrochloric acid solution contains 0.100 moles of hydrochloric acid?

volume (dm³) = $\frac{\text{number of moles}}{\text{concentration}}$

= $^{0.100}/_{0.500}$

= **0.200 dm³**

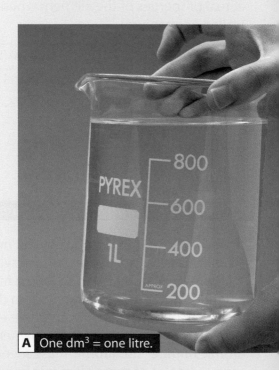

A One dm³ = one litre.

$\text{mass (g)} = M_r \times \text{moles}$

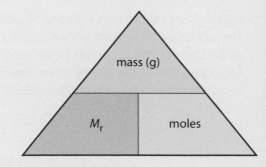

1 Calculate the concentration of a solution of sodium hydroxide containing 0.500 moles in 2.0 dm³ of solution.

2 Calculate the number of moles of hydrochloric acid dissolved in 250 cm³ of a 0.400 mol/dm³ solution.

3 What volume of a 0.100 mol/dm³ solution of sulfuric acid solution contains 0.030 moles?

The concentration of a solution can often be found by an experiment called a titration (see Topic C3.22).

The general rules for all mole calculations are:
1 Calculate the number of moles of the substance whose quantity is known.
2 Use the chemical equation to work out the number of moles of the substance it reacts with or makes.
3 Calculate the concentration, volume or mass of the other substance as required.

Example 4

Vinegar contains ethanoic acid (CH_3COOH). Calculate the concentration of the ethanoic acid, given that 25.0 cm^3 of the vinegar reacts with 20.0 cm^3 of 1.00 mol/dm^3 sodium hydroxide solution.

$$CH_3COOH(aq) + NaOH(aq) \rightarrow CH_3COONa(aq) + H_2O(l)$$

$$\text{moles of NaOH} = \text{concentration} \times \text{volume (dm}^3\text{)}$$
$$= 1.00 \times (^{20.0}/_{1000})$$
$$= 0.020$$
$$\text{moles of } CH_3COOH = \text{moles of NaOH}$$
$$= 0.020$$
$$\text{concentration of } CH_3COOH = \text{moles / volume (dm}^3\text{)}$$
$$= {}^{0.020}/_{(25.0/1000)}$$
$$= \mathbf{0.80 \ mol/dm^3}$$

B Vinegar.

Example 5

Calculate the concentration of potassium hydroxide solution, given that 25.0 cm^3 of it reacts with 22.5 cm^3 of 0.100 mol/dm^3 sulfuric acid.

$$H_2SO_4(aq) + 2KOH(aq) \rightarrow K_2SO_4(aq) + 2H_2O(l)$$

$$\text{moles of } H_2SO_4 = \text{concentration} \times \text{volume (dm}^3\text{)}$$
$$= 0.100 \times (^{22.5}/_{1000})$$
$$= 0.00225$$
$$\text{moles of KOH} = \text{moles of } H_2SO_4 \times 2$$
$$= 0.00225 \times 2$$
$$= 0.0045$$
$$\text{concentration of KOH} = \text{moles / volume (dm}^3\text{)}$$
$$= 0.0045 / (^{25.0}/_{1000})$$
$$= \mathbf{0.180 \ mol/dm^3}$$

Example 6

Calculate the mass of magnesium that reacts with 100 cm^3 of 0.500 mol/dm^3 hydrochloric acid. (Relative atomic mass of Mg = 24)

$$Mg(s) + 2HCl(aq) \rightarrow MgCl_2(aq) + H_2(g)$$

$$\text{moles of HCl} = \text{concentration} \times \text{volume (dm}^3\text{)}$$
$$= 0.500 \times (^{100}/_{1000})$$
$$= 0.050$$
$$\text{moles of Mg} = \text{moles of HCl} \div 2$$
$$= 0.050 \div 2$$
$$= 0.025$$
$$\text{mass of Mg} = M_r \times \text{number of moles}$$
$$= 24 \times 0.025$$
$$= \mathbf{0.6 \ g}$$

4 Calculate the concentration of a nitric acid solution, given that 25.0 cm^3 of this solution reacts with 18.5 cm^3 of 0.200 mol/dm^3 sodium hydroxide solution.
$$HNO_3(aq) + NaOH(aq) \rightarrow NaNO_3(aq) + H_2O(l)$$

5 Calculate the volume of 2.00 mol/dm^3 hydrochloric acid that reacts with 5 g of calcium carbonate. (Relative atomic masses: Ca = 40, C = 12, O = 16)
$$CaCO_3(s) + 2HCl(aq) \rightarrow CaCl_2(aq) + H_2O(l) + CO_2(g)$$

6 Draw a flow diagram to show how to do mole calculations.

Titrations

By the end of this topic you should be able to:

- describe how an acid–alkali titration can be carried out.

Sometimes it is useful to measure the exact concentration of an acid or an alkali. For example, you may wish to find the concentration of the sulfuric acid in a car battery. A very accurate technique called a **titration** is used to do this.

This technique involves taking a known volume of the acid (or alkali) and measuring how much alkali (or acid) is needed to exactly neutralise it. You use an **indicator** to judge when this happens. The point at which it is exactly neutralised is called the **end point**. The indicator changes colour at the end point. If performed well, titrations provide very accurate and precise results.

The volumes of the acid and the alkali used are measured very precisely using a **burette** and a **pipette**. When using a burette, you should take the measurement at the bottom of the meniscus. When using a pipette, the bottom of the meniscus should touch the line.

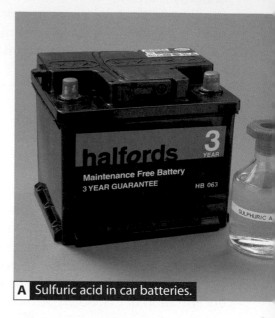

A Sulfuric acid in car batteries.

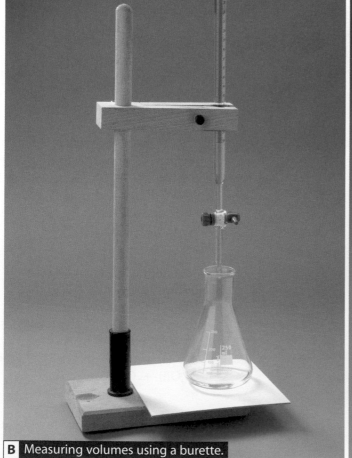

B Measuring volumes using a burette.

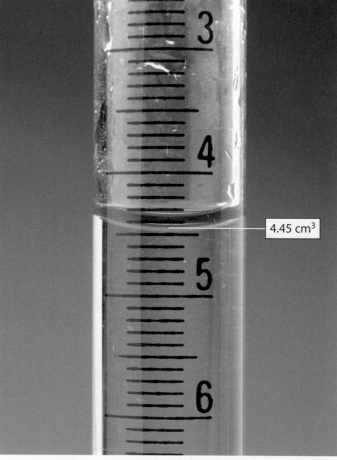

4.45 cm³

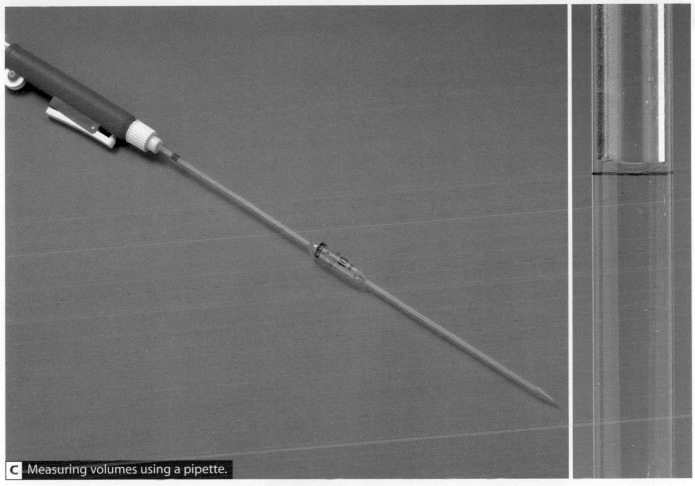

Here is an outline method for carrying out a titration. Usually you put the alkali into the conical flask and the acid in the burette, but it could be done the other way round.

1 Measure out 25 cm³ of the alkali (or acid) into a conical flask using a pipette.

2 Add some indicator.

3 Put the acid (or alkali) into a burette.

4 Add the acid (or alkali) from the burette into the conical flask. Near the end point, which is when the indicator changes colour, add the acid (or alkali) very carefully, drop by drop.

5 Record the final reading on the burette.

6 Repeat the titration.

7 Calculate the mean (average) result.

---

1 What is a titration?

2 a What is the end point of a titration?
 b How can you tell when you have reached the end point?

3 Why should you repeat a titration several times?

4 Why do you use burettes and pipettes rather than measuring cylinders to measure the acid and alkali?

5 Draw a flow diagram to outline how to do a titration.

Choosing indicators for titrations

By the end of this topic you should be able to:

• choose a suitable indicator for a titration.

Indicators are chemicals that are one colour in acid and a different colour in alkali. For example, litmus is red in acid and blue in alkali.

The only exception is universal indicator, which is actually a mixture of indicators. This shows a wide range of colours for different values of pH. Universal indicator should not be used in titrations.

Most indicators do not actually change from their acid colour to their alkali colour at pH 7. For example, methyl orange is red below pH 3.2 and yellow above pH 4.4. It is a mixture of yellow and red, in other words orange, between pH 3.2 and 4.4.

1 What is an indicator?

2 a What is different about universal indicator?
   b How is universal indicator made?

A Colours of some common indicators.

During a titration, the pH changes rapidly at the end point as shown on the graphs (pH curves) in B. For an indicator to work, it must change from one colour to another when the last drop is added at the end point. For a titration between a strong acid and a strong alkali, any indicator would show the end point.

H However, in other titrations the indicator has to be chosen carefully, because it may not change colour at the end point. It might change before or after the end point. For example, if a weak acid is titrated against a strong alkali with methyl orange as indicator, the methyl orange would change from red to yellow before the end point.

Strong acids
hydrochloric acid
sulfuric acid
nitric acid

Weak acids
ethanoic acid
citric acid

Strong alkalis
sodium hydroxide
potassium hydroxide

Weak alkalis
ammonia

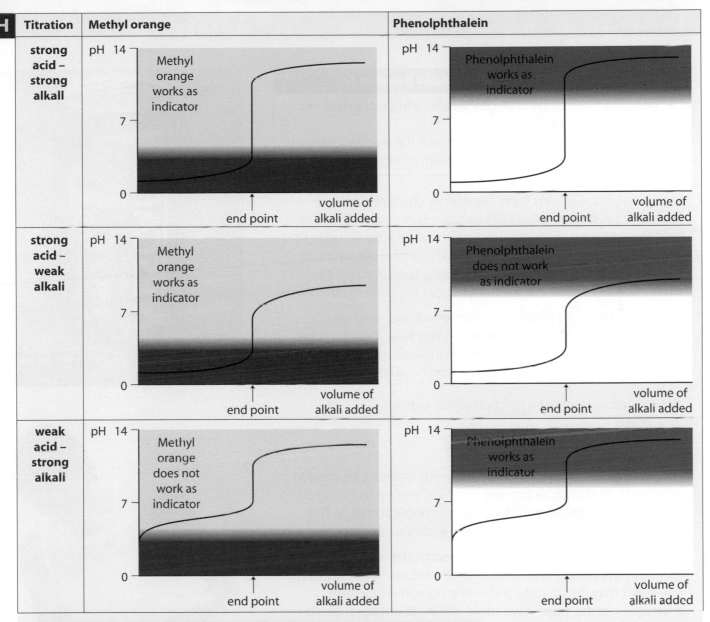

H Titration	Methyl orange	Phenolphthalein
strong acid – strong alkali	Methyl orange works as indicator	Phenolphthalein works as indicator
strong acid – weak alkali	Methyl orange works as indicator	Phenolphthalein does not work as indicator
weak acid – strong alkali	Methyl orange does not work as indicator	Phenolphthalein works as indicator

B Some pH curves for titrations using methyl orange and phenolphthalein.

Table C summarises which indicator can be used in each type of titration.

Acid	Alkali	Indicator
strong	strong	any indicator
strong	weak	some, e.g. methyl orange
weak	strong	some, e.g. phenolphthalein

C Indicators for different types of titration.

3 Which indicator would you use for the following titrations?
  a hydrochloric acid with ammonia
  b ethanoic acid with sodium hydroxide
  c nitric acid and potassium hydroxide.

4 a Explain why phenolphthalein can be used as indicator in a titration between a strong acid and a strong alkali.
  b Explain why phenolphthalein cannot be used as indicator in a titration between a strong acid and a weak alkali.

Energy changes in reactions

By the end of this topic you should be able to:

- describe the energy changes involved in exothermic and endothermic reactions
- draw an energy diagram to represent the energy changes in a reaction, including the activation energy.

In all chemical reactions there are energy changes. Some reactions get hotter. For example, if you react magnesium with acid in a test tube, the test tube gets hotter. Reactions such as that between methane (natural gas) and oxygen give out so much heat that the methane burns. Self-heating cans, used for some drinks, use an exothermic reaction to heat the contents of the can.

Other reactions get colder. For example, if you react sodium hydrogencarbonate with an acid in a test tube, the test tube gets colder. Ice packs, used for sports injuries, work by an endothermic reaction taking place which makes the bag cold.

A Exothermic reactions heat self-heating cans.

1 Give one example of a reaction which gets:
   a hotter
   b colder.

Energy is always conserved, in other words it cannot be created or destroyed. All chemicals possess chemical energy, and different chemicals possess different amounts of chemical energy. This means that there are energy transfers in chemical reactions.

Reactions that get hotter are called **exothermic** reactions. Most reactions are exothermic, although the amount of heat energy given out may be small. In these reactions, the reactants (chemicals at the start) have more chemical energy than the products (chemicals at the end). Energy changes in reactions can represented by an energy diagram.

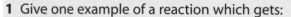

chemical
energy

reactants

The reactants have more chemical energy than the products, so some chemical energy is transferred to heat energy. This means it gets hotter.

chemical energy → heat energy

products

B Endothermic reactions cool ice packs.

2 **a** What is an exothermic reaction?
   b Why do exothermic reactions get hotter?

3 Draw an energy diagram for this reaction which is exothermic:
$$CH_4 + 2O_2 \rightarrow CO_2 + 2H_2O$$

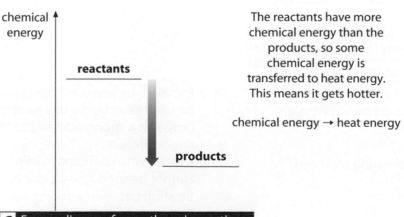

C Energy diagram for exothermic reactions.

Reactions that get colder are called **endothermic** reactions. Not many reactions are endothermic. In these reactions, the reactants have less chemical energy than the products.

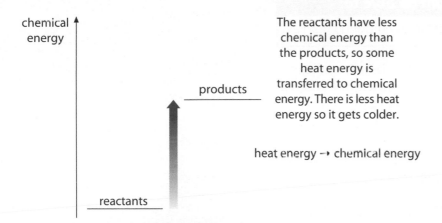

The reactants have less chemical energy than the products, so some heat energy is transferred to chemical energy. There is less heat energy so it gets colder.

heat energy ⟶ chemical energy

D Energy diagram for endothermic reactions.

The energy change for a reaction is often called ΔH, where Δ is a Greek letter called 'delta'.

All reactions need some energy to get started. The **activation energy** is the minimum amount of energy needed to start a reaction. This energy is needed to break some bonds in the reactants. Catalysts are chemicals that speed up reactions without being used up themselves. They work by providing a different route for a reaction that has a lower activation energy. This can be represented on an energy diagram.

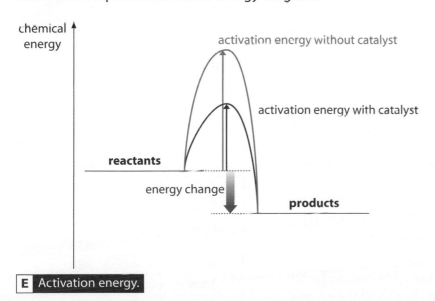

E Activation energy.

6 a What is the activation energy of a reaction?
  b Explain how catalysts speed up reactions.

4 a What is an endothermic reaction?
  b Why do endothermic reactions get colder?

5 Draw an energy diagram for this reaction which is endothermic:
$CuCO_3 \longrightarrow CuO + CO_2$

7 When hydrochloric acid reacts with magnesium, an exothermic reaction takes place. When hydrochloric acid reacts with sodium hydrogencarbonate, an endothermic reaction takes place.
  a What is the difference between exothermic and endothermic reactions?
  b Explain the difference in terms of energy transfers.

Bond energies

H **By the end of this topic you should be able to:**

- calculate the energy change in a reaction using bond energies.

Breaking a bond requires energy. For example, breaking the bond between two chlorine atoms requires 242 kJ/mol. When a bond is made between two chlorine atoms, 242 kJ/mol of energy is released.

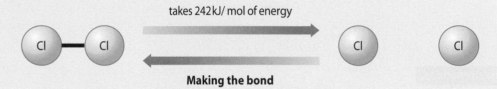

Breaking the bond

takes 242 kJ/ mol of energy

Making the bond

releases 242 kJ/ mol of energy

A Making and breaking bonds.

The amount of energy it takes to break a bond is known as the **bond energy**. Some bond energies are given in Table B.

1 The bond energy for the O=O bond is 498 kJ/mol. What happens in terms of energy when:
   a an O=O bond is broken?
   b an O=O bond is made?

2 Which bond shown in Table B is:
   a the strongest?
   b the weakest?

We can use bond energies to calculate the energy change (ΔH) in chemical reactions:
1 Calculate the energy required to break all the bonds in the reactants.
2 Calculate the energy released in making all the bonds in the products.
3 Energy change (ΔH) = (energy required to break bonds) – (energy released in making bonds).

In an exothermic reaction, the energy released in making bonds is more than the energy required to break bonds, so the energy change has a negative value. In an endothermic reaction, the energy released in making bonds is less than the energy required to break bonds, so the energy change has a positive value.

Bond	Bond energy (kJ/mol)
Br–Br	193
C–Br	276
C–C	348
C=C	612
C–H	412
C=O	743
H–Br	366
H–H	436
N–H	388
N≡N	944
O–H	463
O=O	498

B A range of bond energies.

Example 1

Calculate the energy change in this reaction using bond energies from Table B.

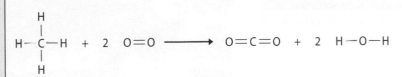

Bonds broken: 4 × (C–H) = 4 × 412 = 1648
2 × (O=O) = 2 × 498 = 996
Total 2644 kJ/mol

Bonds made: 2 × (C=O) = 2 × 743 = 1486
4 × (O–H) = 4 × 463 = 1852
Total 3338 kJ/mol

Energy change = 2644 – 3338 = **–694 kJ/mol**

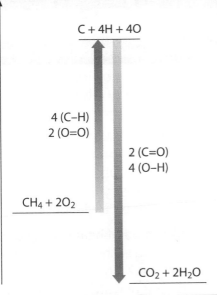

chemical energy

C + 4H + 4O

4 (C–H)
2 (O=O)

2 (C=O)
4 (O–H)

$CH_4 + 2O_2$

$CO_2 + 2H_2O$

Example 2

Calculate the energy change in this reaction using bond energies from Table B.

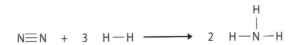

Bonds broken: 1 × (N≡N) = 1 × 944 = 944
3 × (H–H) = 3 × 436 = 1308
Total 2252 kJ/mol

Bonds made: 6 × (N–H) = 6 × 388 = 2328 kJ/mol

Energy change = 2252 – 2328 = **–76 kJ/mol**

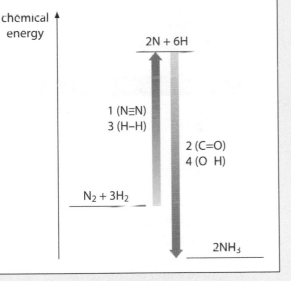

chemical energy

2N + 6H

1 (N≡N)
3 (H–H)

2 (C=O)
4 (O H)

$N_2 + 3H_2$

$2NH_3$

3 For each of the following reactions:
  a Calculate the energy change.
   (i)

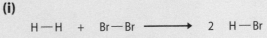

   (ii)

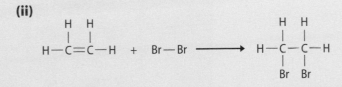

  b State whether the reaction is exothermic or endothermic.

4 a Draw a flow diagram to show how the energy change for a reaction can be calculated from bond energies.
  b Explain why a reaction is exothermic in terms of bond energies.
  c Explain why a reaction is endothermic in terms of bond energies.

Energy in fuels

By the end of this topic you should be able to:

- describe how simple calorimetry can be used to measure the energy released when a fuel or food is burned.

For many reactions we can measure the energy change by simple **calorimetry**. The heat energy given out (or taken in) is used to heat up (or cool down) a known mass of water. We can use calorimetry to compare the amount of energy produced by different fuels and foods.

It takes 4.2 J of heat energy to make 1 g of water 1°C hotter. This figure is known as the **specific heat capacity** of water, which is 4.2 J/g/°C. It therefore takes 8.4 J of heat energy to make 2 g of water 1°C hotter, or to make 1 g of water 2°C hotter. More examples are shown in Table B.

A Burning methane.

Mass of water	1 g	1 g	100 g	200 g
Temperature rise	1°C	2°C	1°C	10°C
Heat required	4.2 J	2 × 4.2 = 8.4 J	100 × 4.2 = 420 J	200 × 10 × 4.2 = 8400 J

B Heat energy required to heat water.

We can calculate the heat energy given out (or taken in) using this equation:

$$\text{heat energy} = \text{mass of water} \times \text{specific heat capacity} \times \text{change in temperature}$$
$$q = mc\Delta T$$

1 How much heat energy is required to make:
  a 10 g of water 5°C hotter?
  b 50 g of water 20°C hotter?
  c 1 kg of water 8°C hotter?

A common way to do the experiment for liquid fuels is to burn the fuel in a spirit burner under a copper can or glass beaker containing a known mass of water. The temperature rise and the mass of fuel burned are measured. The container holding the water to be heated is called a **calorimeter**.

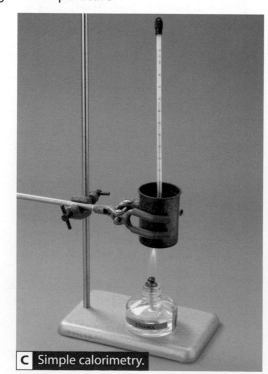

C Simple calorimetry.

Example 1

When 0.25 g of hexane (C_6H_{14}) is burned in a spirit burner, it makes 100 g of water in a copper calorimeter 27°C hotter.

a Calculate the heat released in the experiment.
b Calculate the energy released when hexane is burned. Give the answer in kJ/g.

a Heat released = $mc\Delta T$
$\qquad\qquad$ = 100 × 4.2 × 27
$\qquad\qquad$ = 11 340 J
$\qquad\qquad$ = 11.34 kJ

b Heat released by 0.25 g of hexane = 11.34 kJ
$\quad$ heat released by 1 g of hexane $\quad$ = 11.34 / 0.25
$\qquad\qquad\qquad\qquad\qquad\qquad\qquad$ = 45.4 kJ

$\quad$ Therefore, heat released when hexane is burned = **45.4 kJ/g**

Example 2

When 0.18 g of octane (C_8H_{18}) is burned in a spirit burner, it makes 120 g of water in a copper calorimeter 14°C hotter. (Relative atomic masses: C = 12, H = 1)

a Calculate the heat released in the experiment.
b Calculate the energy change when octane is burned. Give the answer in kJ/mol.

a Heat released = $mc\Delta T$
$\qquad\qquad$ = 120 × 4.2 × 14
$\qquad\qquad$ = 7056 J
$\qquad\qquad$ = 7.056 kJ

b M_r of octane (C_8H_{18}) = (8 × 12) + (18 × 1) = 114
$\quad$ heat released by 0.18 g of octane = 7.056 kJ
$\quad$ heat released by 1 g of octane $\quad$ = 7.056 / 0.18
$\qquad\qquad\qquad\qquad\qquad\qquad\qquad$ = 39.2 kJ

$\quad$ heat released by 1 mole (114 g) of octane = 39.2 × 114
$\qquad\qquad\qquad\qquad\qquad\qquad\qquad\qquad\qquad$ = 4469 kJ

$\quad$ Therefore, energy change = **–4469 kJ/mol** (the sign is negative because it is an exothermic reaction).

---

2 For each of the fuels shown in the table, calculate
  a the heat released per gram
  b the heat released per mole.
  (Relative atomic masses: C = 12, H = 1)

Fuel	Mass burned	Mass of water heated	Temperature rise
Methane (CH_4)	0.12 g	100 g	15°C
Pentane (C_5H_{12})	0.23 g	150 g	17°C

3 Write a paragraph to explain the basic theory of calorimetry to a fellow student. Include what information you need to know and how you get this information in your answer.

Burning fuels

By the end of this topic you should be able to:

- evaluate the social, economic and environmental consequences of burning fuels.

A Humans have always burned fuels.

Issues with fuels

Fuels have many uses. One important use is to provide energy for cars and lorries. They are also important in providing heat to keep us warm and to generate electricity (by heating water to make steam to drive turbines). Humans have burned fuels throughout our history, from burning wood on fires in the Stone Age. We would struggle to survive without using fuels.

B Petrol is used to fuel some cars.

C Fuels are burned to generate electricity.

However, there are problems with using fuels. Many fuels cause air pollution when burned.

Pollutant	How it is formed	Problems it causes
Carbon dioxide (CO_2)	Burning fuels containing carbon.	global warming
Carbon monoxide (CO)	Burning fuels containing carbon in a poor supply of air.	toxic
Carbon / soot (C)	Burning fuels containing carbon in a poor supply of air.	Blackens buildings and causes global dimming.
Sulfur dioxide (SO_2)	Many fossil fuels contain sulfur which produces sulfur dioxide when burned.	Causes acid rain and respiratory problems.
Nitrogen oxides (NO, NO_2)	Formed at very high temperatures in engines and furnaces, from nitrogen and oxygen in the air reacting with each other.	Causes acid rain and respiratory problems.

D Common air pollutants produced by fuels.

1 Why are fuels important to life?

2 What problem is thought to be caused by burning fuels containing carbon?

3 List some pollutants produced by burning petrol in car engines. Petrol is a mixture containing mainly hydrocarbons.

Most of the fuels that we burn are fossil fuels such as coal, oil and gas. These are **non-renewable** and cannot be replaced when we have used them. If we continue to use up non-renewable fuels, we may cause problems for people in the future when there will be little left. However, some fuels are **renewable**. Wood is renewable because more trees can be grown to replace the wood that is burned.

As the demand for energy in the world increases, more and more fuels are being used up. Ways need to be found to reduce this. A key part of this is to make factories, machines, vehicles and other devices more energy efficient. For example, cars and car engines are being developed that use less energy or use energy from renewable sources.

Nuclear fuels are also used to generate electricity. Nuclear fuels do not actually burn but decay radioactively, giving out heat energy. They do not produce carbon dioxide and they will last for thousands of years, but there are concerns over what to do with the radioactive waste materials from nuclear power stations.

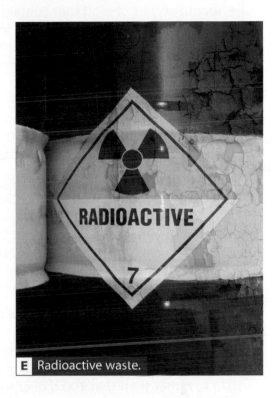

E Radioactive waste.

4 a What is a non-renewable fuel?
  b Give one example.

5 a What is a renewable fuel?
  b Give one example.

6 Give one advantage and one disadvantage of using nuclear fuels.

Different fuels are suitable for different jobs. Fuels that are gases can be easily moved by pipeline but not by road or rail. Solid or liquid fuels are easy to transport by road or rail. Some fuels catch fire very easily, while others are more difficult to ignite. Some fuels burn with a clean flame; some with a smoky flame. Some fuels provide more energy than others; some are more expensive than others. There are many factors to consider when choosing a fuel for a specific job.

7 Write a magazine article about the social, economic and environmental consequences of burning fuels. You should consider whether fuels are renewable or not, how much they cost and the pollution they may cause.

Energy in food

By the end of this topic you should be able to:

- identify types of food that contain a lot of energy
- explain the link between energy in food and obesity
- calculate the energy stored in some foods.

Nutritional values

Different foods contain different amounts of energy. Many foods show nutritional information on the packet. This usually lists how much energy, fat, carbohydrate, protein, fibre and other substances are in foods.

The energy information on food packets is usually given in joules (J) or kilojoules (kJ). People also talk about **calories** (cal) when discussing energy in food, but they usually mean kilocalories (kcal). For example, the label might show that there are 516 kilocalories (516 000 calories) in 100 g, not 516 calories. One kilocalorie equals 4.2 kilojoules.

The data is always given per 100 g of food. However, it is often given per portion as well, which can be more helpful. For example, if you are eating a bag of crisps with a mass of 50 g, it may be more useful to know that the whole packet provides 1078 kJ rather than that 100 g of crisps would provide 2156 kJ.

Different foods contain different amounts of energy. Foods with high proportions of carbohydrates, fats and oils contain relatively large amounts of energy.

Eating food containing more energy than our body needs can result in us putting on weight. Two-thirds of UK adults are overweight. People who are significantly overweight are said to be **obese**. Almost a quarter of UK adults are obese. People who are overweight or obese are far more likely to suffer from health problems such as heart disease, high blood pressure and strokes. If somebody wants to lose weight, they should either eat food containing less energy so that they eat only the amount that their body needs, or do more exercise to use up energy, or a combination of the two.

A Nutritional label on crisps.

B Some high energy foods.

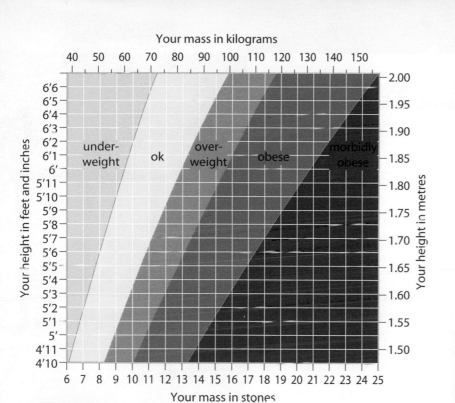

Your mass in kilograms

C Mass chart.

1 Why do people usually become overweight?

2 What does *obese* mean?

3 What is the problem with being overweight or obese?

4 How do people usually lose weight?

5 Which type of foods contain the most energy?

The energy content of foods is measured, like that of fuels, by calorimetry. The methods used in the food industry are more sophisticated, using a bomb calorimeter, but are based on the same principles.

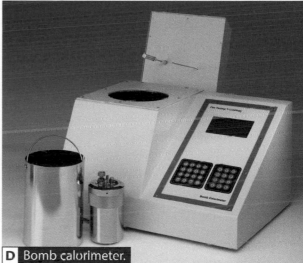

D Bomb calorimeter.

Example 1

When 0.2 g of a biscuit was burned under a boiling tube containing 20 g of water, the temperature rose by 45°C. Calculate the energy content of the biscuit in kJ per 100 g. The specific heat capacity of water is 4.2 J/g/°C.

heat released = $mc\Delta T$

$= 20 \times 4.2 \times 45$

$= 3780$ J

$= 3.78$ kJ

heat released by 0.2 g of biscuit $= 3.78$ kJ

heat released by 1 g of biscuit $= 3.78 / 0.2$

$= 18.9$ kJ

heat released by 100 g of biscuit $= 18.9 \times 100$

$= 1890$ kJ

Therefore energy content of biscuit = **1890 kJ per 100 g**

---

6 When 0.1 g of sugar was burned under a boiling tube containing 10 g of water, the temperature rose by 40°C. Calculate the energy content of the sugar in
   a kJ per 100 g
   b kcal per 100 g (1kcal is the same as 4.2kJ).

7 Explain why is it important to know the energy content of food.

C3.29

Reactions in solution

By the end of this topic you should be able to:

• calculate the energy change for reactions in solution.

Many chemical reactions take place in solution. Some involve two solutions reacting together, including many neutralisation reactions, while others involve a solid reacting with a solution. You can use calorimetry to work out the energy change for such reactions.

When burning fuels or foods, you use the heat from the reaction to heat up some water in a separate container. When doing reactions in solution, the solution itself is heated up by the heat energy released in the reaction. Some reactions in solution are endothermic, and in these reactions the solution gets colder. The reaction is usually done in a well-insulated cup with a lid to try to avoid heat loss.

If you know the quantities of chemicals involved, the mass of water in the solution and the temperature change, you can work out the energy change for the reaction.

A Typical experiment.

Example 1

When 50 cm^3 of 1.0 mol/dm^3 nitric acid was mixed with 50 cm^3 of 1.0 mol/dm^3 sodium hydroxide, the temperature of the solution rose by 6.8°C. Calculate the energy change for the reaction in kJ/mol. The specific heat capacity of water is 4.2 J/g/°C.

$$HNO_3(aq) + NaOH(aq) \rightarrow NaNO_3(aq) + H_2O(l)$$

total volume of solution = 100 cm^3
total mass of water = 100 g (1 cm^3 of water has a mass of 1 g)
heat released = $mc\Delta T$
= 100 × 4.2 × 6.8
= 2856 J
= 2.856 kJ

moles of HNO$_3$ = concentration × volume (dm^3)
= 1.0 × ($^{50}/_{1000}$)
= 0.050

moles of NaOH = concentration × volume (dm^3)
= 1.0 × ($^{50}/_{1000}$)
= 0.050

In this reaction 0.050 moles of HNO$_3$ reacts with 0.050 moles of NaOH.
energy released when 0.050 moles react = 2.856 kJ
energy released when 1 mole reacts = 2.856 / 0.050
= 57.1 kJ

Therefore energy change = **–57.1 kJ/mol** (the sign is negative because it is an exothermic reaction).

Example 2

When 50 cm³ of 0.20 mol/dm³ copper sulfate was mixed with an excess of magnesium powder, the temperature of the solution rose by 25.1°C. Calculate the energy change for the reaction in kJ/mol. The specific heat capacity of water is 4.2 J/g/°C.

$$CuSO_4(aq) + Mg(s) \rightarrow Cu(s) + MgSO_4(aq)$$

volume of solution = 50 cm³
mass of water   = 50 g (1 cm³ of water has a mass of 1 g)
heat released   = $mc\Delta T$
                              = 50 × 4.2 × 25.1
                              = 5271 J
                              = 5.271 kJ

moles of $CuSO_4$ = concentration × volume (dm³)
                              = 0.20 × ($^{50}/_{1000}$)
                              = 0.010

energy released when 0.010 moles react = 5.271 kJ
energy released when 1 mole reacts   = 5.271 / 0.010
                                                          = 527 kJ

Therefore energy change = **−527 kJ/mol** (the sign is negative because it is an exothermic reaction).

---

1 When 25 cm³ of 2.0 mol/dm³ hydrochloric acid was mixed with 25 cm³ of 2.0 mol/dm³ ammonia solution, the temperature of the solution rose by 12.4°C. Calculate the energy change for the reaction in kJ/mol. The specific heat capacity of water is 4.2 J/g/°C.

$$HCl(aq) + NH_3(aq) \rightarrow NH_4Cl(aq)$$

2 When 30 cm³ of 1.5 mol/dm³ hydrochloric acid was mixed with an excess of sodium hydrogencarbonate powder, the temperature of the solution fell by 11.0°C. Calculate the energy change for the reaction in kJ/mol. The specific heat capacity of water is 4.2 J/g/°C.

$$NaHCO_3(s) + HCl(aq) \rightarrow NaCl(aq) + H_2O(l) + CO_2(g)$$

3 a Explain the principle involved in calculating the energy change for a reaction in solution.
   b Draw a flow diagram to show how to calculate the energy change.

Investigative Skills Assessment

When copper sulfate solution reacts with zinc powder, an exothermic reaction takes place heating up the solution. The aim of this investigation is to find out how changing the mass of zinc affects the temperature change in the reaction.

Ben and Rebecca reacted 50 cm³ of 1.0 mol/dm³ copper sulfate solution with different masses of zinc. They did the experiment twice. Their results are in the table.

	Set of results 1					Set of results 2				
Mass of zinc (g)	1.0	2.0	3.0	4.0	5.0	1.0	2.0	3.0	4.0	5.0
Start temperature (°C)	21	21	20	20	21	20	20	21	20	20
Final temperature (°C)	33	44	55	58	58	31	33	55	57	58
Temperature rise (°C)										

1 Look at the values of the independent variable.
   a What was the interval between these measurements? *(1 mark)*
   b What range of values was used for the independent variable? *(1 mark)*

2 Copy the table then calculate the temperature rise in each experiment and write it into the blank spaces in your table. *(1 mark)*

3 **a** One of the results is anomalous. Which one? *(1 mark)*
   b Do you think that this anomalous result is due to a random error or a systematic error? Explain your answer. *(2 marks)*
   c Suggest a reason for this anomalous result. *(1 mark)*

4 Calculate the mean temperature rise for each mass of zinc and write it into a table like the one below. Do not include the anomalous result in your calculation. *(1 mark)*

Mass of zinc (g)	1.0	2.0	3.0	4.0	5.0
Temperature rise (°C)					

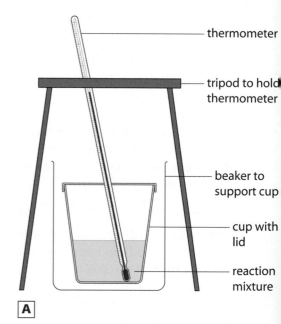

thermometer

tripod to hold thermometer

beaker to support cup

cup with lid

reaction mixture

A

5 Which would be the best way of presenting the results from this experiment? Choose from the following *(1 mark)*:
   bar chart   line graph   pie chart   histogram

6 What could Ben and Rebecca do to improve the reliability of their results? *(1 mark)*

7 Ben and Rebecca said that their results showed that using more zinc gives a bigger temperature rise, but that there was a point at which increasing the mass of zinc had no effect.
   a Do you agree with this conclusion? Explain your answer. *(1 mark)*
   b At approximately what mass of zinc does increasing the mass of zinc have no further effect? *(1 mark)*
   c ✎ What could Ben and Rebecca do to find out at what point increasing the mass of zinc has no effect? Quality of written communication is important in your answer to this question. *(3 marks)*

Glossary

activation energy Minimum energy needed to start a chemical reaction.

alkali metals Elements in Group 1 of the Periodic Table.

atomic number Number of protons in an atom (proton number).

H atomic spectrometer Instrument used to analyse elements.

H bond energy Amount of energy required to break a covalent bond.

burette Glass tube with a tap for measuring solutions very precisely.

calcium hydrogencarbonate Soluble compound that causes temporarily hard water.

calcium sulfate Soluble compound that causes permanently hard water.

calorie A unit for energy.

calorimeter Metal or glass container of water used in an experiment to find the energy change for a reaction.

calorimetry Experimental technique to measure the energy change in a reaction.

carbonates Compounds containing ions with the formula CO_3^{2-} which are detected by the production of carbon dioxide when acid is added.

catalyst Substance that speeds up a chemical reaction but does not get used up.

chlorinate Add chlorine to water to kill bacteria.

crystallise Form crystals.

displacement reaction Reaction in which a more reactive element takes the place of a less reactive element.

element Substance containing only one type of atom.

H empirical formula Simplest ratio of atoms of each element in a compound.

end point Moment in a titration at which an acid has been neutralised by an alkali.

endothermic Reaction that gets colder; the products have more chemical energy than the reactants.

exothermic Reaction that gets hotter; the products have less chemical energy than the reactants.

filter bed Area containing sand and gravel, or carbon, through which water moves and is purified.

flame test Means of identifying some metal ions by the colour of the flames that they produce.

H gas–liquid chromatography Method of separating gases using the principles of chromatography.

group Vertical column in the Periodic Table.

halides Compounds containing ions formed from the Group 7 halogens.

halogens Elements in Group 7 of the Periodic Table.

hard water Water containing dissolved calcium and/or magnesium ions.

hydrated Containing water.

indicator Substance that is a different colour in acids and alkalis.

H infrared spectroscopy Means of analysing organic compounds.

ion exchange column Column where calcium and magnesium ions are exchanged by sodium ions.

ionise Split up into ions.

limescale Calcium carbonate formed when temporarily hard water is boiled.

H line emission spectrum Series of lines produced by an atomic spectrometer, used to detect different elements.

H mass spectrometer Instrument used to analyse both elements and compounds.

nitrates Compounds containing ions with the formula NO_3^-.

non-renewable Type of resource that cannot be replaced.

H nuclear magnetic resonance spectroscopy Means of analysing organic molecules.

obese Very overweight.

organic compound Compound that contains carbon (and often hydrogen).

period Horizontal row in the Periodic Table.

Periodic Table A list of all the elements in order of atomic number.

permanently hard water Water containing calcium sulfate or magnesium sulfate that cannot be softened by boiling.

pipette Glass tube for measuring solutions very precisely.

precipitate Insoluble substance formed when two solutions mix and react.

H proton acceptor Substance that accepts protons from acids – also called a base.

H proton donor Substance that gives protons (hydrogen ions) to other substances – also called an acid.

proton number Number of protons in an atom (atomic number).

renewable Type of resource that can be replaced.

saturated hydrocarbon Containing only carbon-carbon single bonds.

saturated solution Solution in which no more solute will dissolve at that temperature.

sodium carbonate Compound used to soften water, because it removes calcium ions.

sodium hydroxide Solution used to detect some metal ions and the ammonium ion.

soft water Water that does not contain dissolved calcium and/or magnesium ions.

soften Remove the hardness from water.

solubility Number of grams of solute that dissolve in 100 g of water or other solvent at a given temperature.

solute Solid that dissolves in a solvent to form a solution.

solvent Liquid in which a solute dissolves to form a solution.

specific heat capacity Amount of heat energy needed to make 1 g of a substance 1°C hotter.

sulfates Compounds containing ions with the formula SO_4^{2-}.

temporarily hard water Water containing calcium hydrogencarbonate that is softened by boiling.

titration Experimental technique to measure the amount of substance in a solution.

transition metals Block of metals in the Periodic Table between Groups 2 and 3.

H **ultraviolet spectroscopy** Means of analysing nitrate and phosphates in water.

unsaturated hydrocarbon Containing carbon–carbon double bonds.

unsaturated solution Solution in which more solute can be dissolved at that temperature.

water cycle Continuous process by which water is transferred between the surface of the Earth and the atmosphere.

water filter Commercially bought device used to remove dissolved impurities from tap water.

1 The table gives the solubility of potassium chlorate at various temperatures.

Temperature (°C)	Solubility (g per 100 g of water)
10	5
20	7.5
30	10.5
40	14
50	18.5
60	24
70	30
80	38
90	46

a Plot a solubility curve to show these values. *(4 marks, HSW)*

b What is the solubility of potassium chlorate at 25°C? *(1 mark)*

c Describe how the solubility of solids varies with temperature. *(1 mark)*

d How does the solubility of gases vary with temperature? *(1 mark)*

e A solution of potassium chlorate containing 25 g of potassium chlorate per 100 g of water was cooled. At what temperature would crystals start to appear? *(1 mark)*

f The same solution was cooled to 20°C. What mass of crystals would be formed? *(1 mark)*

2 Dot was given a sample of water to analyse. She boiled the water to dryness and then performed the following tests on the dry residue.

a A flame test showed a brick-red flame. What metal ion was present? *(1 mark)*

b She added hydrochloric acid to the sample. It produced a gas that turned limewater cloudy. What ion was present? *(1 mark)*

c Give the formula of the compound that was present in the dry residue. *(1 mark)*

d This compound was not in the original water sample. Where had it come from? *(1 mark)*

e Give a balanced symbol equation showing how this compound was formed. *(2 marks)*

3 Dot also measured the pH of the water. It was pH 8.

a What is the Brønsted–Lowry definition of an acid? *(1 mark)*

b How does the Brønsted–Lowry idea of an acid differ from that of Arrhenius? *(2 marks)*

c A pH of 8 indicates the presence of a weak alkali. What does this mean? *(1 mark)*

4 a ▣ The empirical formula of an organic hydrocarbon compound was found by combustion analysis. 0.42 g of the compound was burnt completely in air and formed 1.32 g of carbon dioxide and 0.54 g of water. What is the compound's empirical formula? *(3 marks)*

b What is the name of the instrument that could be used to find the relative formula mass of this compound? *(1 mark)*

5 This question is about the Periodic Table.

a How are elements placed in order in the Periodic Table? *(1 mark)*

b Mendeleev is known as the 'father of the Periodic Table'. He followed the work of John Newlands but left gaps for undiscovered elements in his table. Why were Mendeleev's ideas accepted by other scientists? *(2 marks, HSW)*

c In what group is the element with electronic structure 2,8,4? *(1 mark)*

6 This question is about the elements in Group 1 of the Periodic Table.

a What is Group 1 called? *(1 mark)*

b Potassium reacts with water.

(i) Will this reaction be more or less reactive than that of sodium with water? *(1 mark)*

(ii) Explain why. *(3 marks)*

7 The table below shows the nutritional information for three food products. The data shows the content per 100 g of the food.

Food	Energy (kJ)	Energy (kcal)	Protein (g)	Carbohydrates (g)	Fat (g)	Fibre (g)
A	1541	367	4.1	53.2	17.1	2.6
B	206	49	0.4	13.8	0.2	2.4
C	391	93	2.5	21.2	0.1	2.0

a Which food contains the least energy? *(1 mark)*
b (i) What is obesity? *(1 mark)*
(ii) What causes obesity? *(1 mark)*
(iii) Which of these three foods in a person's diet would lead to obesity most easily? *(1 mark, HSW)*

8 Many people see hydrogen as the fuel of the future and expect it to replace petrol and diesel for cars. Some cars are already being made that are fuelled by hydrogen (H_2), but these are very expensive at the moment.
a Give two disadvantages of burning petrol and diesel in cars. *(2 marks)*
b Explain why burning hydrogen does not cause any air pollution. *(1 mark)*

9 Sarah performed a titration to find the concentration of a bottle of drain cleaner containing sodium hydroxide solution. She titrated 25 cm³ of the drain cleaner against 2.00 mol/dm³ hydrochloric acid. She repeated the experiment three times.

$$HCl(aq) + NaOH(aq) \rightarrow NaCl(aq) + H_2O(l)$$

a Name a suitable indicator for this titration. Sodium hydroxide is a strong alkali and hydrochloric acid is a strong acid. *(1 mark)*
b Explain why Sarah did the titration three times. *(1 mark, HSW)*
c The drain cleaner reacted with 30.5 cm³ of 2.00 mol/dm³ hydrochloric acid. Calculate the concentration of the sodium hydroxide in the solution. *(3 marks)*

10 A student burned 0.15 g of a fuel under a copper calorimeter containing 100 g of water. The water temperature rose by 23°C.
a Calculate the heat released by the fuel in this experiment in J. The specific heat capacity of water is 4.2 J/g/°C. *(2 marks)*
b Calculate the heat released by the fuel in kJ/g. *(1 mark)*

Forces and energy in space

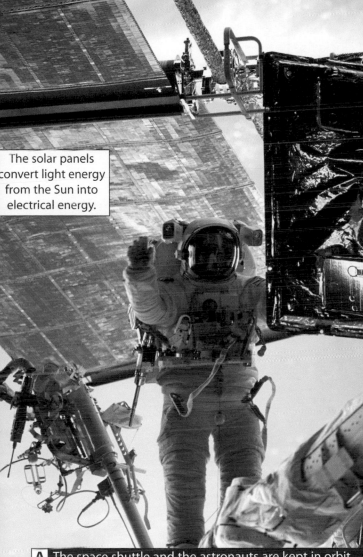

The solar panels convert light energy from the Sun into electrical energy.

A The space shuttle and the astronauts are kept in orbit around the Earth by the force of gravity.

B This astronaut is using a power tool to undo bolts. The power tool produces a turning force.

Forces can speed things up or slow them down, make things start or stop moving, or change the direction in which they are moving. In this unit you will look at forces that turn things and how forces can keep things moving in circles.

By the end of this unit you should be able to:

- describe how forces have a turning effect
- explain what keeps bodies turning in a circle
- recall what provides the centripetal force for planets and satellites
- describe the life history of stars.

1 Draw a concept map to show what you know about forces and movement.

2 We live in the Solar System. Write a set of bullet points to show what you know about the Sun and the planets.

3 Why is the Sun important for life on Earth?

Moments

By the end of this topic you should be able to:

- recall that the turning effect of a force is called the moment
- use the equation for calculating moments
- understand that if a body is not turning, the total clockwise moment must be exactly balanced by the total anticlockwise moment about any axis
- calculate forces or distances on balanced objects.

You use a turning force every time you open a door or turn on a tap. The turning effect of a force is called a **moment**.

The moment of a force depends on how big the force is, and also on where the force is applied. For example, you can push a door closed more easily if you push near the handle. If you try pushing near the hinge, it takes a much bigger force to close the door.

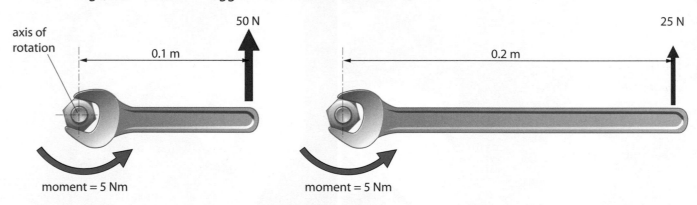

50 N
axis of rotation
0.1 m
moment = 5 Nm

Short spanner needing a large force.

25 N
0.2 m
moment = 5 Nm

This spanner is longer, so a small force gives the same turning moment.

A The moment of a force depends on its size and the perpendicular distance from the axis of rotation.

The size of a turning force can be calculated using the following equation. The unit for moments is the **newton metre** (**Nm**).

moment (in newton metres, Nm)
= force (in newtons, N) * perpendicular distance from line of action of force to axis of rotation (in metres, m)

Example

You pull on a door with a force of 3 N. The handle is 70 cm from the hinges. What is the moment at the hinges?

moment = force × perpendicular distance
= 3 N × 0.7 m
= 2.1 Nm

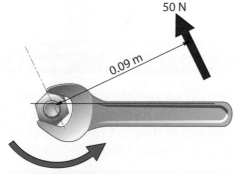

50 N
0.09 m
moment = 4.5 Nm

If you do not pull at right angles to the spanner, not all of the force is used to produce a moment. The moment depends on the perpendicular distance from the line of action of the force to the axis of rotation.

1 Why is it harder to close a door if you push it near the hinges?

2 Why is it easier to steer a bicycle if you hold the ends of the handlebars instead of holding them near the middle?

3 A mechanic uses a 50 cm long spanner and exerts a force of 20 N. What moment does she produce?

4 The photo shows some lock gates that control the level of water in a canal.

Where is the best place to push to open the gates? Explain your answer.

H If an object is not turning, then any turning forces on it must be balanced. The clockwise moments are equal to the anticlockwise moments.

90 N

axis of rotation

450 N

1.0 m

0.2 m

B The wheelbarrow is not turning, because the clockwise and anticlockwise moments are balanced.

5 The load in the wheelbarrow is reduced to 100 N. What force does the gardener need to apply to the handles to hold the back legs just off the ground?

6 Ben weighs 400 N and is sitting 1.5 m from the centre of a see-saw. Jill weighs 300 N. How far away from the centre does she have to sit to make the see-saw balance?

7 a Explain why undoing a nut is easier if you use a long spanner.

H b Write a set of instructions explaining how to calculate where two people of different weights should sit on a see-saw so that it balances.

Centre of mass

By the end of this topic you should be able to:

- describe what is meant by the centre of mass of a body
- recall that the centre of mass of a symmetrical body is along the axis of symmetry
- explain that a suspended body will come to rest with its centre of mass directly below the point of suspension
- describe how to find the centre of mass of a thin sheet of a material.

1 What does 'centre of mass' mean?

2 a Draw a square and mark the centre of mass on it.
   b Explain how you worked out your answer to part **a**.

You can balance a ruler by putting your finger under the middle of it. The weight of the ruler acts as if it is all concentrated in one point in the middle of the ruler. This point is called the **centre of mass**. For a symmetrical object, the centre of mass is along the axis of symmetry.

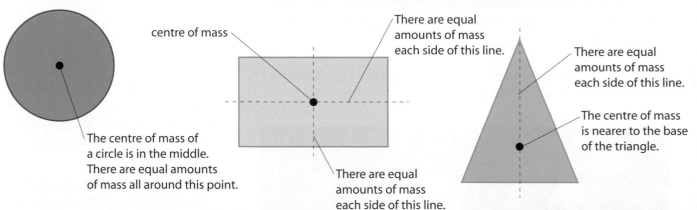

centre of mass

There are equal amounts of mass each side of this line.

There are equal amounts of mass each side of this line.

The centre of mass of a circle is in the middle. There are equal amounts of mass all around this point.

There are equal amounts of mass each side of this line.

The centre of mass is nearer to the base of the triangle.

A Positions of the centre of mass of different shapes.

If you hang an object from something, it will come to rest with its centre of mass directly below the point where it is suspended. We can use this idea to find the centre of mass of an object.

point of suspension

centre of mass

B The centre of mass is directly below the point of suspension.

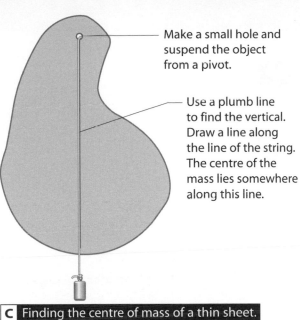

Make a small hole and suspend the object from a pivot.

Use a plumb line to find the vertical. Draw a line along the line of the string. The centre of the mass lies somewhere along this line.

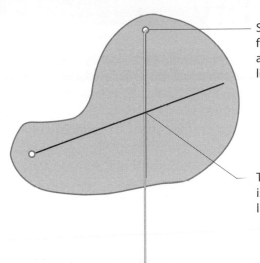

Suspend the object from a different point, and use the plumb line again.

The centre of mass is where the two lines meet.

C Finding the centre of mass of a thin sheet.

3 Look at the diagrams in C.
  a Describe in your own words how to find the centre of mass of a thin sheet of material.
  b Explain why this method works.

4 Describe how you could find the centre of mass of a hexagonal sheet of metal *without* using the method you described in question **3**.

5 Copy the following objects, and mark where you think their centres of mass are.

  a

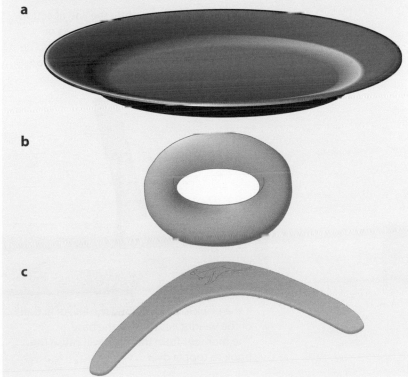

  b

  c

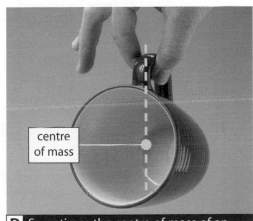

centre of mass

D Sometimes the centre of mass of an object is at a place where there is no material.

6 What can you say about where the shopping has been put in this basket? Explain your answer in as much detail as possible, using the phrase 'centre of mass'.

Stability

P

H | *By the end of this topic you should be able to:*

- analyse the stability of bodies by considering their tendency to topple
- recognise the factors that affect the stability of a body
- explain that if the line of action of the weight of a body lies outside the base of the body, there is a resultant moment and the body will tend to topple.

Stability is the tendency of a body to stay in a particular position. A book lying on its side is **stable**, because it tends to stay that way. A book standing on one end is **unstable**, because it will fall over very easily.

The stability of a body depends on where its centre of mass is in comparison to its base. The base does not have to be solid – the area enclosed by the four legs of a chair is the 'base' of the chair.

A

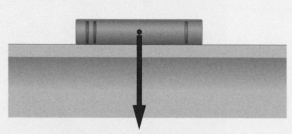

The weight of a body acts downwards from the centre of mass.

If the book is tilted slightly, the line of action of the weight still lies within the area of the book that was resting on the bench. The book will fall back into its original position.

The book can stand on one end because the line of action of the weight passes through its base.

If the book is tilted slightly, the line of action of the weight lies outside the base. The moment from this force will cause the book to topple over.

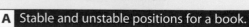

A | Stable and unstable positions for a book.

The stability of an object can be increased by:
- making its centre of mass lower
- giving it a wider base.

If the centre of mass is lower, the object has to be tilted further before the line of action of its weight lies outside the base.

1 Why is it difficult to balance a pencil on one end?

2 Why does giving an object a wider base make it more stable?

3 Look at photo B. Suggest why the stone does not tip over when people stand on the end of it.

B The Cantilever Stone in Snowdonia.

It is important to design objects so that they are stable when in use. Unstable objects that fall over easily can injure people or cause damage.

C A bus being tested for stability.

4 a Why is it important that buses are stable?
  b Where should passengers sit on a double-decker bus to give the bus most stability? Explain your answer.

5 Look at the drinking glasses in photo D.
  a Which one is the most stable?
  b Which is the least stable?
  c Explain your answers to parts **a** and **b**.

6 How does filling a drinking glass affect its stability? Explain your answer.

D Different styles of drinking glasses.

7 a List three different objects where stability is important.
  b Explain how the design of these objects helps them to be stable.

133

Circular motion

By the end of this topic you should be able to:

- identify which forces provide the centripetal force in a given situation
- interpret data on bodies moving in circular paths
- recall that when a body moves in a circle, it continuously accelerates towards the centre of the circle
- describe what centripetal force is, and in which direction it acts
- explain how the centripetal force changes if the mass or speed of the body changes, or if the radius of the circle changes.

You may not think of a motorbike going round a bend at a constant speed as accelerating, but it is! **Acceleration** is a change in **velocity**, and velocity depends on both the speed at which something is moving, and on the direction in which it is moving.

A force is needed to cause any acceleration. For motion in a circle, this force is called the **centripetal force** and it always acts towards the centre of the circle. In the case of the motorbike, the centripetal force is provided by friction between its tyres and the road surface. The motorcycle is continuously accelerating towards the centre of the circle.

centripetal force

direction changing

A The centripetal force is provided by friction between the tyres and the road.

B The centripetal force is provided by forces from the wings.

C A fairground ride.

1 What is centripetal force?

2 Look at photo B. The aircraft are travelling at a constant speed. Are they accelerating? Explain your answer.

3 Look at photo C. What is providing the centripetal force?

Force, mass and acceleration are related to each other by the formula force = mass × acceleration. The force needed to produce circular motion therefore depends on both the mass and the acceleration.

The stone has changed direction by this angle in one second.

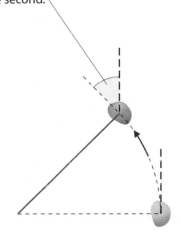

If the stone is swung faster, it changes direction by a bigger angle each second. This greater acceleration requires a bigger centripetal force.

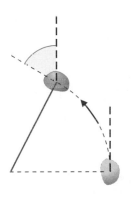

If the string is shorter, the stone changes direction by a bigger angle each second. This greater acceleration requires a bigger centripetal force.

D A higher speed and a smaller circle both need a bigger centripetal force.

The amount of centripetal force needed to keep an object moving in a circle therefore depends on:
- the mass of the object – the greater the mass, the larger the force needed
- the speed at which it is travelling – the higher the speed, the larger the force needed
- the radius of the circle – the smaller the circle, the larger the force needed.

4 Look at photo C. How would the centripetal force be changed if:
  a the ride went faster?
  b the ride went round a shallower curve?
  c there were all adults in the seats instead of children?

5 A lorry and a car are both going around a bend at the same speed. Which one has the greater centripetal force acting on it? Explain your answer.

6 a How do mass, speed and radius affect the size of the centripetal force needed to keep something moving in a circle?
  b Give three examples of circular motion which have different kinds of centripetal force.

Gravity and the Solar System

By the end of this topic you should be able to:

- explain that all bodies attract each other with a force called gravity, and that this force depends on the masses of the bodies and the distance between them
- explain that the orbits of the planets are ellipses with the Sun at one focus, and that gravity provides the centripetal force that allows them to stay in orbit
- explain that the further away a planet is from the Sun, the longer it takes to make a complete orbit
- recall that to stay in orbit around the Sun a planet must move at a particular speed
- interpret data on planets moving in approximately circular orbits.

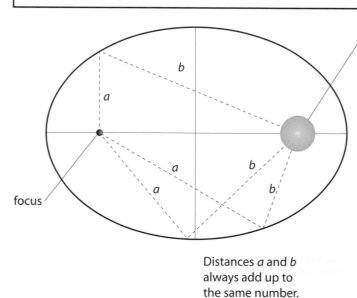

An ellipse has two foci. For a planet's orbit, the Sun is at one focus of the ellipse.

b

a

a

a

b

b

focus

Distances *a* and *b* always add up to the same number.

The Earth's orbit is almost circular.

149 567 950 km

149 597 870 km

A The foci of an ellipse, and the Earth's almost circular orbit.

There are eight planets in the Solar System, which all move in **elliptical** orbits around the Sun. An ellipse is like a squashed circle. However, the orbits of some of the planets are almost circular, so when we are thinking about how they stay in orbit we can use ideas about circular motion.

Inside an ellipse there are two points each called a **focus**, as shown in diagram A. A circle is an ellipse with both foci at the centre.

The centripetal force that keeps the planets in orbit around the Sun is **gravity**. All objects attract each other with a force called gravity. The size of the force depends on the masses of the bodies and how far apart they are.

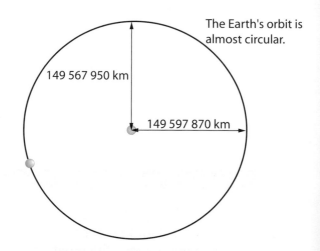

All objects attract each other.

If one or both of the objects has more ma the force is bigger.

If the objects are further apar the force is sma

B The force of gravity between two objects depends on their masses and the distance between them.

1 a What shape is the orbit of the Earth around the Sun?
  b Why can we use ideas about circular motion to think about the Earth's orbit?

2 What is the centripetal force that keeps the planets orbiting around the Sun?

3 Which is bigger: the force of gravity between the Moon and the Sun, or the force of gravity between the Earth and the Sun? Explain your answer.

4 Look at Table C.
  a Which planet in Table C is furthest from the Sun?
  b How does the length of a year change with the distance of a planet from the Sun?

5 Suggest how long the years of these dwarf planets might be:
  a Pluto (orbits beyond Neptune)
  b Ceres (orbits between Mars and Jupiter).

Planet	Length of year
Mercury	88 days
Venus	225 days
Earth	365 days
Mars	687 days
Jupiter	11.86 years
Saturn	29.46 years
Uranus	84.01 years
Neptune	164.79 years

C Year lengths of the planets. The units are Earth days and Earth years.

The further a planet is from the Sun, the longer it takes to orbit the Sun once. This is partly because the more distant planets have longer orbits, but also because they move more slowly. A planet must move at the correct speed to stay in orbit at a particular distance from the Sun.

H

For the same speed of movement, if the radius of the circle is twice as big, the force needed is only half.

Force needed to keep a planet in orbit around the Sun.

For a planet, if the distance from the Sun doubles, the force of gravity acting on it is only a quarter of its original value. If the planet still moved at the same speed, the force would not be big enough to keep it moving in a circle. The planet stays in a stable orbit only if it is also moving more slowly.

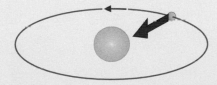

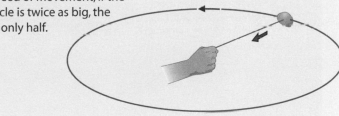

D Relationship between speed and distance of a stone and a planet.

The speed of a planet in its orbit does not depend on its mass. The force needed to keep a body in circular motion does increase as the mass of the body increases, but the force of gravity between two bodies also increases if the mass increases, so the two effects cancel each other out.

6 a Why is the force of the Sun's gravity on Mars and that on Earth different?
  b Describe all the differences you can between the orbits of Mars and Earth, and explain why they are different.

Changing ideas

By the end of this topic you should be able to:

- distinguish between models based on evidence and those based on non-scientific ideas
- explain that hypotheses or scientific models can be used to make predictions that can be tested
- explain that if the theories and models we have available do not completely match our data or observations, then we need to check the validity of our observations or data, or to amend the theories or models.

There are five planets in our Solar System that can be observed with the naked eye: Mercury, Venus, Mars, Jupiter and Saturn. For thousands of years astronomers made careful observations of the positions of these planets against the stars, and used their observations to work out a **model** of what we now call the Solar System. Most early ideas had the Earth at the centre of the Universe. One such idea was published by an Egyptian astronomer called Ptolemy in the 2nd century CE.

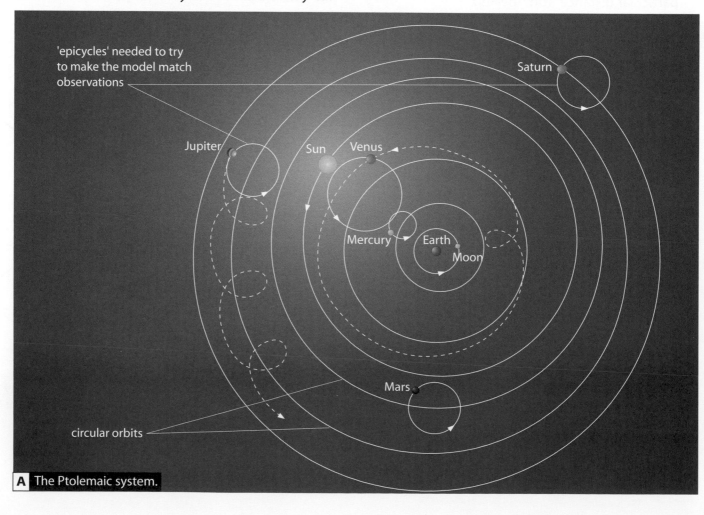

'epicycles' needed to try to make the model match observations

Saturn

Jupiter

Sun

Venus

Mercury

Earth

Moon

Mars

circular orbits

A The Ptolemaic system.

Although Ptolemy's model still did not accurately predict the motions of the planets, it was accepted by astronomers for over 1500 years. One major problem with the Ptolemaic model was that it did not explain why the planets did not always appear to move smoothly from west to east across the fixed stars in the sky, but sometimes had more complicated movements.

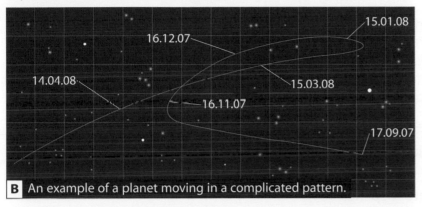

15.01.08
16.12.07
14.04.08
15.03.08
16.11.07
17.09.07

B An example of a planet moving in a complicated pattern.

1 What evidence is there that the stars move around the Earth?

2 a Describe Ptolemy's model of the Solar System.
  b What predictions could be made using Ptolemy's model?
  c Did observations match the predictions made? Explain your answer.

In 1543 a Polish astronomer called Nicolas Copernicus (1473–1543) published a book which suggested that the Sun was at the centre of the Universe, and the Earth and the other planets moved in circular orbits around the Sun. This model matched observations better, but not exactly. This idea was in direct conflict with the teachings of the Christian church, which held that God had created the Earth, and that the Earth was at the centre of the Universe.

3 Which model of the Solar System (that of Copernicus or the church) was based on scientific ideas? Explain your answer.

Galileo Galilei (1564–1642), using the newly invented telescope, observed moons moving around Jupiter. This was the first evidence that bodies could move around something other than the Earth. Tycho Brahe (1546–1601) made many accurate observations of the movements of the planets, and Johannes Kepler (1571–1630) used these observations to work out the model of the Solar System that we use today. Kepler's laws described the planets moving in elliptical orbits around the Sun, speeding up slightly when they were nearer the Sun, and slowing down again when further away.

When Sir Isaac Newton (1642–1727) worked out how the force of gravity changes with the masses of objects and the distances between them, it helped to explain why the planets moved in the way they do.

4 What observation did Galileo make that supported the idea that the Earth was not at the centre of the Solar System?

5 a How did Kepler modify Copernicus' model?
  b Why did he do this?
  c Why was Tycho Brahe's work important for Kepler?

6 Suggest why Kepler's model of the Solar System is accepted today.

7 Give examples from the text above of:
  a a model based on evidence
  b a model based on non-scientific ideas
  c a model being changed to match new evidence.

Satellites

By the end of this topic you should be able to:

- interpret data on satellites moving in orbits that approximate to circular paths
- recall how the speed of a satellite and the time for an orbit depend on its distance from the Earth
- recall that communications satellites are usually put into a geostationary orbit above the equator, and monitoring satellites are usually put into a low polar orbit.

A **satellite** is any body that orbits around another body. The Moon is a natural satellite of the Earth, but there are also thousands of artificial satellites moving around the Earth.

The time a satellite takes to orbit the Earth depends on its distance from the Earth. The higher the orbit, the longer the satellite takes to complete one orbit. When a satellite is launched, engineers must work out the exact speed it needs to be travelling to stay in its orbit. The type of orbit needed depends on what the satellite will be used for. The satellite has to be moving at the correct speed to stay in an orbit at a particular distance from the Earth.

Communications satellites are used for transmitting TV signals, telephone calls and so on. People receiving the signals need to have their receiving dish pointing at the satellite, so these satellites are put into **geostationary orbits** above the equator. Weather satellites are also sometimes put into geostationary orbits.

1 a What is special about a satellite orbiting 35 768 km above the Earth?
b What is this kind of orbit called?
c Why is it useful?

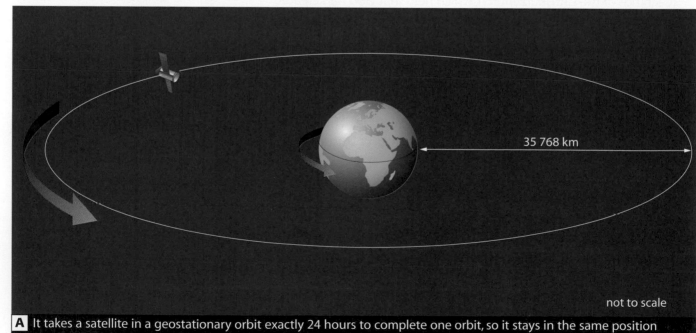

35 768 km

not to scale

A It takes a satellite in a geostationary orbit exactly 24 hours to complete one orbit, so it stays in the same position above the Earth.

Many other types of satellite are put into lower orbits, and the orbits may also be at an angle to the plane of the equator. If the orbit passes over the poles, it is referred to as a **polar orbit**. **Monitoring satellites** that detect vegetation, snow cover or other features of the Earth are often put into polar orbits.

2 a How long does a satellite in a lower orbit take to complete one orbit, compared to a satellite in a geostationary orbit?
b Which satellite is moving faster?

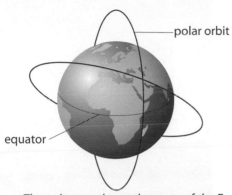

The pale area shows the parts of the Earth a satellite in a polar orbit can monitor during one orbit. The whole Earth can be covered over a series of orbits.

B Low Earth orbits.

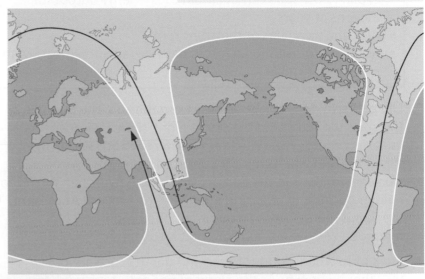

C Satellite imagery is very useful after natural disasters. This image shows damage caused by a tsunami in Indonesia at the end of 2006.

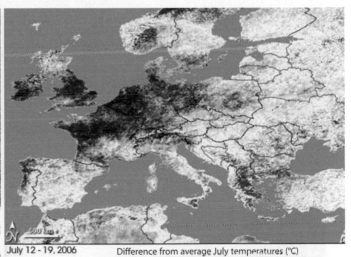

July 12 - 19, 2006   Difference from average July temperatures (°C)

-10   0   10

D Data can be gathered from satellites over many years to show changes from normal values. This map shows the temperatures in Europe during the heatwave in July 2006.

3 The satellite that took photo C is in a polar orbit 700 km above the Earth.
  a Suggest one advantage of orbiting at this height. (*Hint*: think about the detail in the photograph.)
  b Why do you think this satellite has been put in a polar orbit?

4 Suggest an advantage of putting a weather monitoring satellite into:
  a a geostationary orbit
  b a low polar orbit.

5 Which type of orbit would you select for the following uses? Explain your answers.
  a A satellite to monitor the sizes of the Arctic and Antarctic ice caps
  b A satellite to relay TV programmes
  c A military satellite to take pictures of an enemy country's defences.

Stars and planets

By the end of this topic you should be able to:

- explain how stars can maintain their energy output for millions of years
- describe how stars and planets form
- recall that gravitational forces balance radiation pressure to make a star stable.

Life on Earth depends on energy from the Sun. The Sun, like all the **stars** we can see in the sky at night, shines because it is releasing energy from **nuclear fusion reactions** within it. When the Sun was formed, it consisted mainly of hydrogen. Nuclear reactions in the Sun are converting hydrogen **nuclei** to helium nuclei, and releasing energy in the process. At present, the Sun is about 70% hydrogen, and the proportion of hydrogen will get less as more of it is converted to helium.

Stars form when clouds of dust and gas in space are pulled together by gravity. As the cloud of gas gets denser, it heats up and may begin to glow. As more and more mass is attracted, the temperatures and pressures in the centre become high enough to force hydrogen atoms to **fuse** together and form helium. The star starts to produce much more energy, which causes **radiation pressure**. The radiation pressure tries to make the star expand, but this is balanced by gravitational forces and so the star's size is stable. Stars can produce energy and remain stable for millions of years.

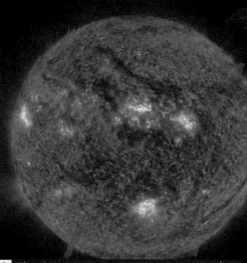

A The Sun gives out nearly 4×10^{26} J of energy every second, and has been doing so for about 4.5 billion years.

1 How long ago was the Sun formed?

2 What produces the energy that the Sun gives out?

3 Why will the Sun eventually stop shining?

B The Eagle nebula, one of the places where new stars are forming in our galaxy.

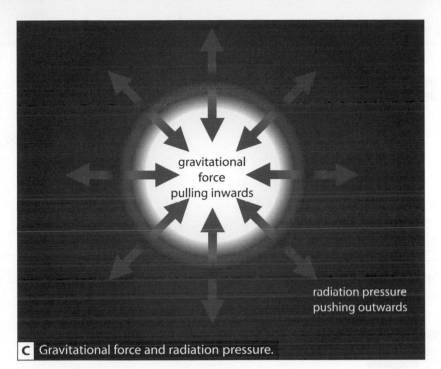

C Gravitational force and radiation pressure.

4 a What force is trying to make the Sun expand?
b What stops the Sun expanding?

How did the planets form?

Many different explanations have been suggested for how the planets formed. The current idea is the **nebular hypothesis**, which was first suggested in 1775. This hypothesis agrees with most of the information we have at the moment, although if new information is found the hypothesis may have to be changed.

The nebular hypothesis suggests that the cloud of dust and gas that formed the Sun was spinning, and the spin made it flatten out into a disc. The gas towards the edges of the disc cooled down and began to clump together into grains. Grains moving around the disc bumped into each other and stuck together, and gradually bigger and bigger bodies built up. The gravity from these bigger bodies attracted more dust and grains, and eventually these became the planets. The asteroids are the bodies that did not grow big enough to become planets.

D An artist's impression of the Solar System forming.

5 a Describe how the planets might have formed.
b Why do you think this description is called a 'hypothesis'?

6 Write a brief history of the Solar System. Present your history as a fact sheet, or as an illustrated web page, using images from the

Life cycles of stars

P

By the end of this topic you should be able to:

- recall that our Sun is one of the many billions of stars in the Milky Way galaxy, and that the Universe is made up of billions of galaxies
- describe the life cycles of stars of similar size to the Sun, and of stars much larger than the Sun
- **H** • explain how new elements can be formed inside stars.

If you look up at the night sky on a dark night you can see millions of stars. Most of the stars you can see are in our own **galaxy**, the Milky Way. The Sun is just one of the many billions of stars in the Milky Way. There are billions of other galaxies in the **Universe**.

A The M100 galaxy. Astronomers think the Milky Way galaxy looks similar to this.

P

1 a What is a galaxy?
  b What is our galaxy called?

Astronomers have studied millions of different stars, and have discovered that stars have a **life cycle**. What happens to a star as it gets older depends on how big it is.

Stars that are about the size of our Sun remain stable until they have 'burnt up' most of their hydrogen fuel. When this happens the core of the star will collapse, but its outward layers will expand to form a **red giant** star. It will remain as a red giant for about a billion years before ejecting a shell of gas and dust called a **planetary nebula** (although it has nothing to do with planets!). The rest of the star will shrink to form a white dwarf star. No nuclear reactions happen inside a **white dwarf**, and it will gradually cool over about a billion years.

B When the Sun becomes a red giant, the Earth will become too hot for life to exist. The Earth may even be destroyed.

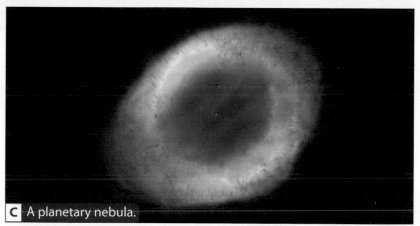

C A planetary nebula.

Stars considerably more massive than the Sun become **red supergiants**, but then instead of throwing off a planetary nebula the star will explode. The explosion is called a **supernova**. For very big stars, what is left will shrink to form a **black hole**, which is so dense that not even light can escape from it. If the star is not quite big enough to form a black hole, it will form a small, very dense star called a **neutron star**.

2 a What is a red giant?
  b What is a planetary nebula?
  c What is a white dwarf?

3 What is a supernova?

4 Why won't the Sun form a black hole?

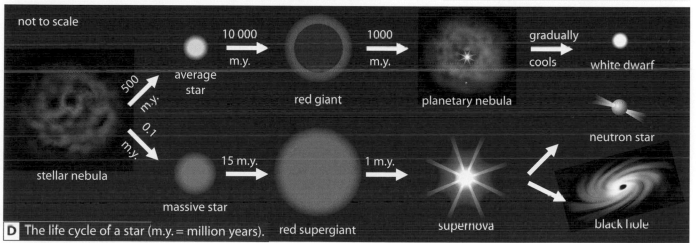

D The life cycle of a star (m.y. = million years).

H When the Universe began, it consisted mainly of hydrogen with a little helium. All the other elements that exist have been created inside stars.

When stars begin to run short of hydrogen, other nuclear reactions start. For example, helium nuclei become converted to carbon nuclei in a sequence of nuclear reactions inside red giants. For stars up to about four times the mass of the Sun, elements up to oxygen can be created in this way.

In more massive stars, elements up to the mass of iron can form by further nuclear reactions. Elements in the Periodic Table beyond iron are created in supernova explosions.

5 a Which elements will eventually be formed in the Sun?
  b How can other elements be formed?

6 Draw a flow chart showing the life cycle of a star:
  a of a similar size to the Sun
  b much bigger than the Sun.

H 7 Explain where the elements in your body came from.

Investigative Skills Assessment

C&R Ltd make home DIY products. The 'SlimShelf' is fastened to the wall by fixings which cannot be seen, and is intended to hold only light objects.

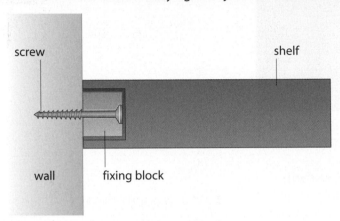

If the moment at the fixing is too large, the shelf can fall off the part of the fixing attached to the wall, so the packaging includes the following warning label:

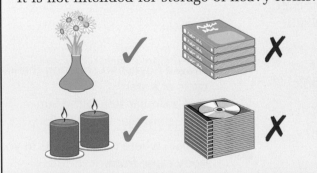

Warning

Due to the concealed nature of the wall fixing, this shelf is intended to hold light objects. It is not intended for storage of heavy items.

C&R Ltd have received some customer complaints about the shelves falling down. The management has asked the testing department to test the shelves and recommend new wording for the packaging that indicates the maximum weight the shelf can hold, instead of just using pictures. Here are their results.

Type of wall	Weight at collapse (N)*
Plasterboard	15.5
Breeze block / plaster	15.8
Brick / plaster	15.0
Wood	15.3

* The weight was positioned as far away from the wall as possible each time.

1 a What was the independent variable in this investigation? *(1 mark)*
b Is this variable a continuous, discrete or categoric variable? *(1 mark)*
c Name one variable that the team would have needed to keep constant to make sure their results were valid. *(1 mark)*
d What was the dependent variable? *(1 mark)*
e Is this variable a continuous, discrete or categoric variable? *(1 mark)*
f What would be the best way to present these results? *(1 mark)*

2 a Does the type of wall that the shelf is fastened to affect the strength of the fixing? *(1 mark)*
b Explain your answer. *(1 mark)*

3 Why did the team position the weight as far from the wall as possible? Use ideas about moments in your answer. *(3 marks)*

4 How could the team check the reliability of their results? Explain your answer. *(1 mark)*

5 The team recommend that the packaging for the shelf should be changed to say:
'Maximum weight on shelf = 10 N'
The management accepted this recommendation, but changed it to say:
'Maximum weight on shelf = 1 kg'
a Explain why the management's label is incorrect scientifically. *(1 mark)*
b ✎ Suggest why the management did this. *(3 marks)*

Investigating space

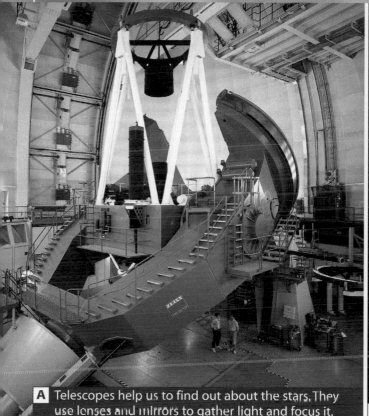

A Telescopes help us to find out about the stars. They use lenses and mirrors to gather light and focus it.

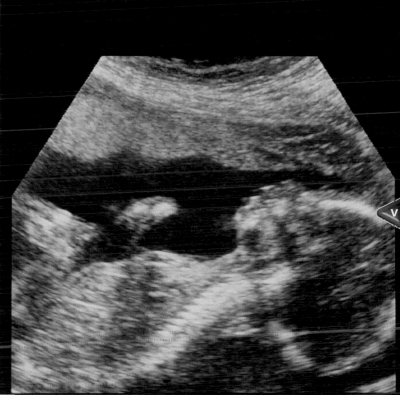

B Ultrasound allows us to see a fetus without harming it.

Scientific theories are based on observations. The first scientific observations were made with eyes and ears, but today most observations require the use of instruments to allow us to measure things, or to allow us to see things that we cannot measure directly.

Most instruments rely on electricity to make them work, or on electric motors to move them.

By the end of this unit you should be able to:

- construct ray diagrams to show how images are formed by mirrors and lenses
- describe sounds in terms of frequency, amplitude and waveform
- explain how ultrasound can be used in medicine and industry
- explain how the motor effect is used in electrical devices
- describe the factors affecting the induction of a potential difference
- **H** explain how generators work
- describe a transformer and what it does.

1 **a** Make a list of all the words you can recall connected with light.
  b Write definitions for as many of the words as you can.

2 Draw a concept map to show what you know about sound waves.

3 Make a list of bullet points to summarise what you know about electricity and magnetism.

Plane mirrors

By the end of this topic you should be able to:

- explain what the normal is
- recall that the angle of incidence is equal to the angle of reflection
- recall different ways of describing an image
- describe the nature of the image produced by a plane mirror
- construct ray diagrams to show the formation of images by plane mirrors.

We see objects when light is reflected by them and enters our eyes. Mirrors are objects that reflect light so well that we can see **images** in them. The simplest kind of mirror is a **plane** (flat) mirror.

Diagram A shows some important terms used when investigating the properties of mirrors. Angles are always measured from the **normal**, which is a line at right angles to the mirror.

When light is reflected by a mirror, the **angle of incidence** is always equal to the **angle of reflection**.

If you look at an image of yourself in a mirror, the image is **upright** (the same way up as you are) and the same size as you. The image also appears to be behind the mirror. The rays of light do not pass through the image but only *appear* to come from it. This kind of image is called a **virtual image**.

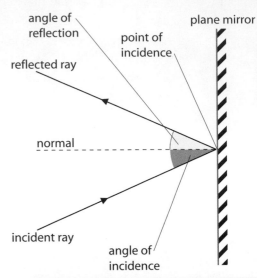

A A ray of light being reflected by a mirror.

1 What do the following words or phrases mean?
   a normal
   b angle of reflection
   c image
   d plane

B A virtual image in a mirror.

C The image produced by a projector is a real image. The rays of light go to the image, and you can touch the image.

The properties of the image in a plane mirror can be explained by constructing a **ray diagram**. Light is reflected by objects in all directions, but to keep ray diagrams simple we draw only a few rays.

2 What is the difference between a real image and a virtual image?

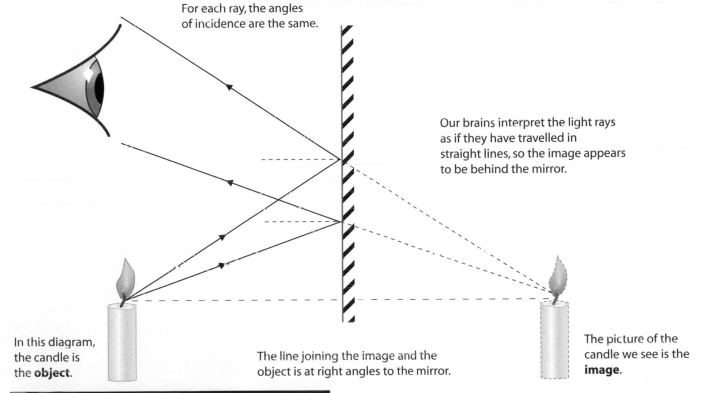

For each ray, the angles of incidence are the same.

Our brains interpret the light rays as if they have travelled in straight lines, so the image appears to be behind the mirror.

In this diagram, the candle is the **object**.

The line joining the image and the object is at right angles to the mirror.

The picture of the candle we see is the **image**.

D Ray diagram showing how a virtual image is formed.

The image in a plane mirror is
- upright
- the same size as the object
- the same distance from the mirror as the object

3 A mug is 8 cm tall, and you place it 10 cm from a mirror.
  a How big does the mug appear to be in the mirror?
  b How far from the mirror does the image of the mug appear to be?

4 a Copy and complete this diagram showing how an image of a light bulb is formed.

E

  b Label your diagram with as many key words from these pages as possible.

Curved mirrors

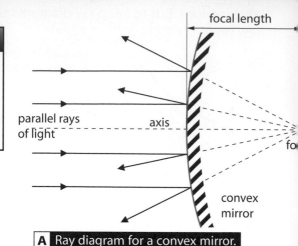

focal length

parallel rays of light

axis

fo

convex mirror

A Ray diagram for a convex mirror.

By the end of this topic you should be able to:

- describe the nature of the image produced by convex and concave mirrors
- calculate the magnification produced by a lens or mirror
- construct ray diagrams to show the formation of images by curved mirrors.

Convex mirrors make rays of light **diverge** (spread out). If you shine a set of parallel rays of light at a convex mirror, they appear to come from a point behind the mirror. This point is called the **focus** of the mirror. The distance between the mirror and the focus is called the **focal length**.

The image formed by a convex mirror is always virtual, upright, and **diminished** (smaller than the object).

1 List the similarities and differences between the image in a convex mirror and the image in a plane mirror.

2 a What is the mirror shown in the photo being used for?
  b Why is a convex mirror used instead of a plane mirror?

Concave mirrors make rays of light **converge** (come together). They produce different kinds of image, depending on how far the **object** is from the mirror. You can draw ray diagrams to help you work out the nature of the image formed by a curved mirror. You need to draw only three rays of light.

B A convex mirror used at an awkward road junction.

concave mirror

We draw the rays through the top of the object.

A ray parallel to the axis of the mirror will be reflected through the focus (F).

F

2F

axis

A ray passing through the focus will be reflected parallel to the axis of the mirror.

The top of the image will be where the rays cross.

A ray passing through a point 2 focal lengths from the mirror (2F) will be reflected back on itself.

C Ray diagram for a concave mirror.

Diagram C shows that for an object more than two focal lengths from the mirror, the image is **inverted** (upside down), diminished and closer to the mirror. Since the rays of light pass through the image, this is a **real image**.

You can work out the magnification of the image using this formula:

$$\text{magnification} = \frac{\text{image height}}{\text{object height}}$$

In diagram C, you can see that the magnification is 0.5.

Distance of object	Nature of image
Further than 2F	real, inverted, diminished, closer to mirror
2F	real, inverted, same size, same distance from mirror
Between 2F and F	real, inverted, magnified, further from mirror
F	no image (reflected rays are parallel to axis)
Closer than F	virtual, upright, magnified, behind mirror

D Images formed by a concave mirror.

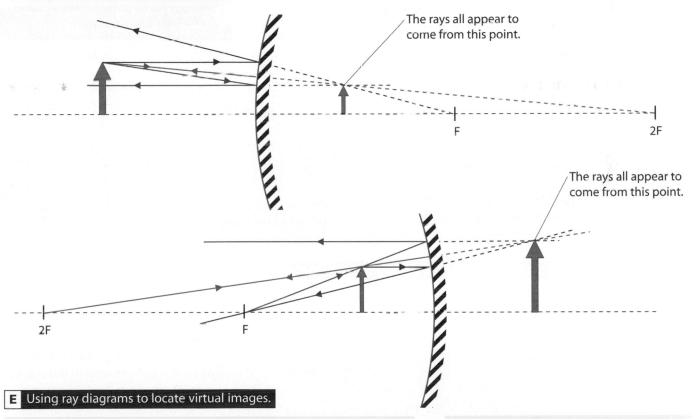

The rays all appear to come from this point.

F   2F

The rays all appear to come from this point.

2F   F

E Using ray diagrams to locate virtual images.

3 'All mirrors produce virtual images.'
  a In what way is this statement correct?
  b Why could the statement be considered to be incorrect?

4 a Draw a ray diagram to show how the image in a concave mirror is formed when the object is $1\frac{1}{2}$ focal lengths from the mirror.
  b Calculate the magnification of the image from your diagram.

5 Concave mirrors can be used as shaving or make-up mirrors. Explain where you would have to hold your face to use the mirror for these purposes.

6 Draw a concept map to summarise the information about curved mirrors on these pages.

Refraction

By the end of this topic you should be able to:

- describe how light is refracted when it passes from one material to another
- describe how light is refracted by a prism.

Light can travel through many different materials, but it travels at different speeds in different materials. As light passes the **interface** between one material and another it changes speed. This change in speed can cause the direction of the light to change. This bending is called **refraction**.

The way the light bends depends on how fast the light travels in the two materials, and the angle at which the light hits the interface. The greater the difference in speed in the two materials, the more the light is bent.

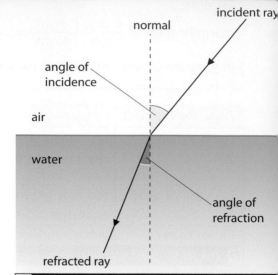

A A ray of light being refracted at the interface between air and water.

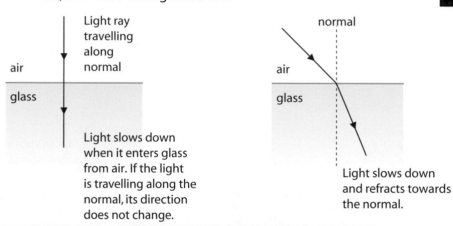

air
glass
Light ray travelling along normal
Light slows down when it enters glass from air. If the light is travelling along the normal, its direction does not change.

normal
air
glass
Light slows down and refracts towards the normal.

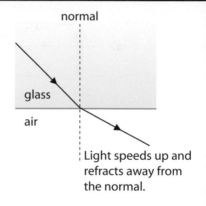

normal
glass
air
Light speeds up and refracts away from the normal.

B Refraction depends on the materials and the angle of incidence.

We can explain what is happening when light is refracting by thinking about waves. Diagram C shows what happens when waves change speed.

1 What is refraction?

2 Light is refracted by a greater angle when it goes from air to glass than when it goes from air to water. What does this tell you about the speed at which light travels in glass and water?

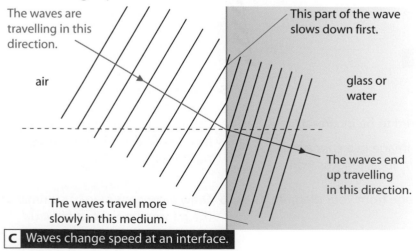

The waves are travelling in this direction.

air

This part of the wave slows down first.

glass or water

The waves end up travelling in this direction.

The waves travel more slowly in this medium.

C Waves change speed at an interface.

'White' light consists of a **spectrum** of light of different colours. Each colour has a different wavelength. All these wavelengths of light travel at the same speed in a vacuum or in air, but they are slowed down by different amounts when they go into glass or water. Red light is refracted by the smallest angle and violet light by the greatest angle. These differences make the colours in white light **disperse** (spread out) when white light is refracted.

3 a Which slows down more when it goes into glass: red light or violet light?
b Explain how you worked out your answer.

You cannot usually see the different colours when light passes into water or through a pane of glass, as the colours are not dispersed very far. A triangular prism can spread the colours out enough for the spectrum to be seen.

D A prism forming a spectrum from 'white' light.

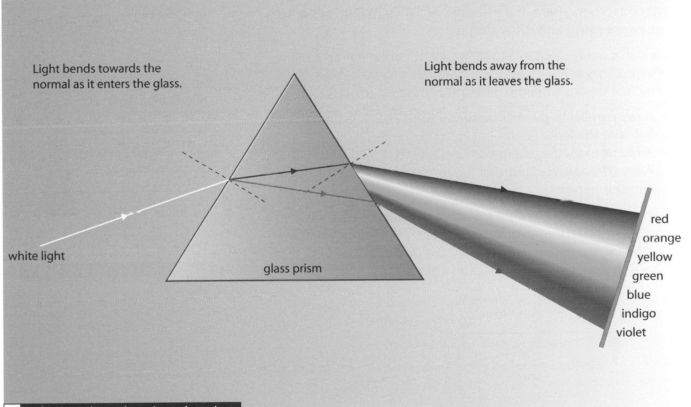

Light bends towards the normal as it enters the glass.

Light bends away from the normal as it leaves the glass.

white light

glass prism

red
orange
yellow
green
blue
indigo
violet

E Refraction through a triangular prism.

4 a What does 'dispersion' mean?
b Why does dispersion happen?

5 Why don't we usually see dispersion when light is refracted through windows?

6 a Draw a diagram of light passing through a glass block, and mark the normals and angles of incidence and reflection on it.

b Draw a diagram of light passing through a prism, and add labels to explain what is happening.

Lenses

By the end of this topic you should be able to:

- describe the nature of the image produced by a diverging lens
- describe the nature of the image produced by a converging lens for an object placed at different distances from the lens
- construct ray diagrams to show the formation of images by diverging and converging lenses
- explain the use of a converging lens as a magnifying glass
- calculate the magnification of an image.

Much of the Universe is too small or too distant to be seen with the naked eye. **Lenses** in microscopes and telescopes have been used for centuries to help us find out about the things around us.

Lenses are pieces of glass or other transparent materials, shaped to bend light in particular ways. Two main types of lens are **converging** and **diverging** lenses.

We can use ray diagrams to help us work out what kind of image a lens will form. As for curved mirrors, we can use three principal rays to work out where the image will be formed:

- A ray parallel to the axis bends so that it passes through the focus of the lens.
- A ray from the focus emerges parallel to the axis.
- A ray through the centre of the lens passes straight through without bending.

Although in reality the light refracts both when it enters the lens and again when it emerges, we can keep ray diagrams simple by combining these two refractions into a single change of direction that happens at the centre of the lens.

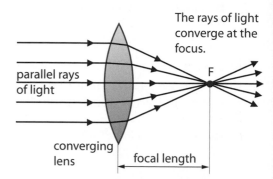

The rays of light converge at the focus.

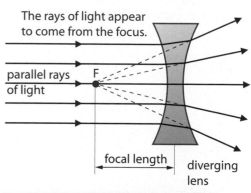

The rays of light appear to come from the focus.

A Converging and diverging lenses.

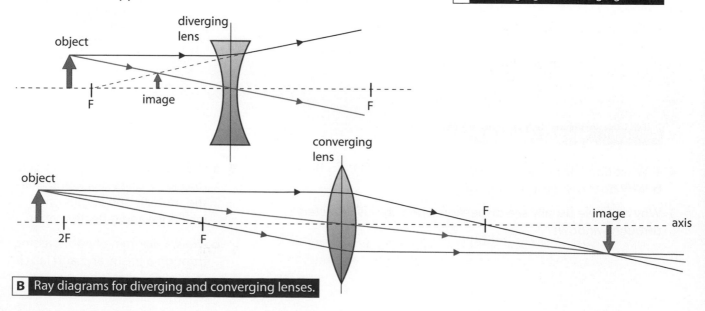

B Ray diagrams for diverging and converging lenses.

Type of lens	Distance of object	Nature of image
Diverging	any	virtual, upright, diminished, closer to lens than object
Converging	further than 2F	real, inverted, diminished, between F and 2F
Converging	2F	real, inverted, same size, at 2F
Converging	between 2F and F	real, inverted, magnified, further than 2F
Converging	F	no image (emerging rays are parallel to axis)
Converging	closer than F	virtual, upright, magnified, same side of lens as object

C Images formed by lenses.

1 Why is the image produced by a diverging lens referred to as a virtual image?

2 Draw a ray diagram to show how an image is formed by a converging lens when the object is between F and 2F.

Diagram D shows how a converging lens can be used as a magnifying glass.

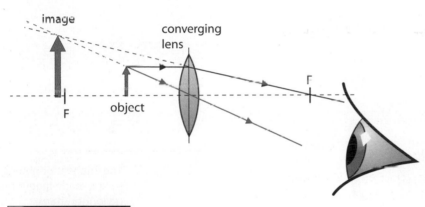

D Magnifying glass.

You can work out the magnification of the image using this formula:

$$\text{magnification} = \frac{\text{image height}}{\text{object height}}$$

3 Is the image formed by a magnifying glass a real or a virtual image?

4 Estimate the magnification of the image in diagram D. Show your working.

5 a Why doesn't a magnifying glass work if it is too far from the object?

b How does the magnification of a magnifying glass change as the object gets closer to the lens? (*Hint*: you may need to draw two ray diagrams.)

6 Write an advert for a lens manufacturer that explains what different kinds of lenses can do.

Cameras

By the end of this topic you should be able to:

- explain the use of a converging lens in a camera to produce an image of an object on a detecting device such as film.

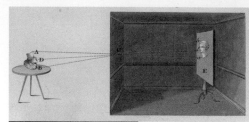

A A camera obscura.

A camera is basically a light-proof box with a small hole in one side. The earliest 'camera obscura' was just a darkened room with a small hole in one wall. Light coming through the hole formed an inverted image on the opposite wall. Some artists used a camera obscura to help them paint pictures.

A pinhole camera is a small version of a camera obscura. It can be made to record a permanent picture if a piece of photographic film is placed inside it. A pinhole camera can be improved by putting a converging lens in the hole. This focuses the light so that a sharp image is formed on the back of the camera.

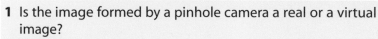

The image is dim because not much light can get through the hole.

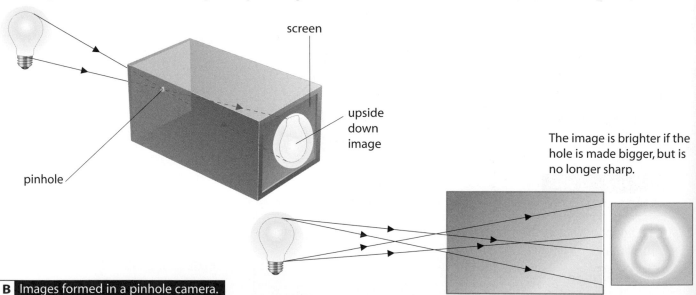

screen

upside down image

pinhole

The image is brighter if the hole is made bigger, but is no longer sharp.

B Images formed in a pinhole camera.

1 Is the image formed by a pinhole camera a real or a virtual image?

2 Explain why making the hole bigger produces:
   a a brighter image
   b a blurred image.

3 How would you work out the focal length needed for a lens in a pinhole camera?

4 Draw a ray diagram to show how a pinhole camera produces a sharp image on the screen.

Even with a lens, a pinhole camera would not produce very good pictures. Modern cameras have a lot more features.

The aperture (opening) can be changed to allow different amounts of light into the camera.

Chemical changes occur in the film when light hits it. These changes are made permanent when the film is developed.

The lens focuses light onto the film.

A shutter stops light getting to the film. The shutter is opened when you take a picture. The length of time the shutter is open can be adjusted.

The lens can be moved to adjust the focus for objects at different distances.

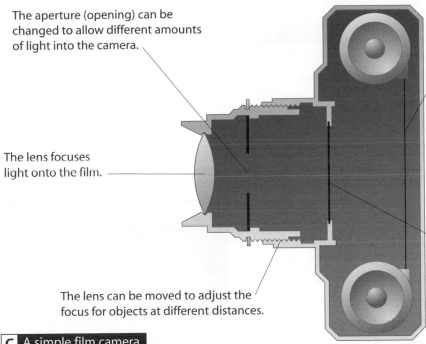

C A simple film camera.

Most modern cameras are digital, and use electronic sensors to detect the image instead of using film. The image in a digital camera is stored electronically and downloaded to a computer for viewing or printing.

D Cameras can be attached to telescopes to take pictures of stars and galaxies. The light from some distant stars is too dim to be seen by the human eye, even with a telescope, but the film or sensors in a camera can be exposed for minutes or hours to allow enough light to be detected.

5 Why does the position of the lens in a camera need to be adjustable?

6 a Describe two ways in which a photographer can reduce the amount of light hitting the film.
  b Suggest when the photographer might want to do this.

7 Explain why lenses are needed in cameras, in as much detail as you can.

Sound

By the end of this topic you should be able to:

- describe how sounds are caused and how they travel
- recall that sound waves can be reflected and refracted
- explain the link between frequency and pitch, and between amplitude and loudness, and compare these on oscilloscope traces
- explain that the quality of a note depends upon the waveform.

Sounds are made when things **vibrate**. A vibrating object causes the air near it to vibrate, and these vibrations are passed through the air as a wave. We hear a sound when the wave reaches our ears. Sound needs a **medium** in which to travel (a solid, a liquid or a gas), so it cannot travel through a vacuum.

We use light to investigate many things, but there are some places where light is not useful. For example, light does not travel very far through sea water, so sound waves are used to investigate the ocean floor. Sound waves are sent down to the sea bed and reflect back from it. The time it takes for the sound to return can be used to calculate the depth of the sea.

Sound waves can also be refracted when they change speed. For example, sound travels faster in water than in air, so the direction of a sound wave changes when it enters water.

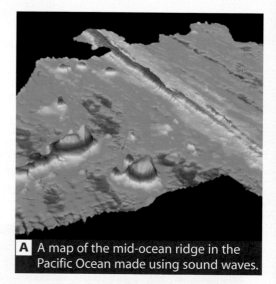

A A map of the mid-ocean ridge in the Pacific Ocean made using sound waves.

1 a Write down three similarities between sound and light.
  b Write down two differences.

Sounds vary in **pitch** (how high or low they sound), in loudness and in quality. We can investigate sounds using an oscilloscope and a microphone. Vibrations in the air are represented as a wave on the oscilloscope screen.

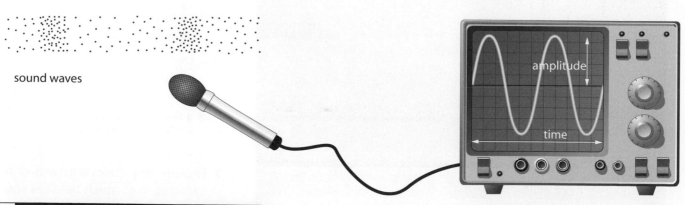

sound waves

B Showing a sound wave on an oscilloscope.

The number of sound waves in one second is called the **frequency**, and is measured in **hertz** (**Hz**). The higher the frequency, the higher the pitch of a note. The loudness of a sound depends on its **amplitude**. The larger the amplitude, the louder the note.

high pitched, quiet note

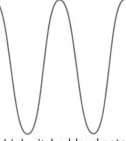
high pitched, loud note

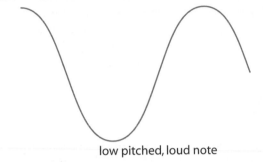
low pitched, loud note

C Oscilloscope traces for different sounds.

2 Fifty sound waves go past a point in 2 seconds. What is the frequency of the sound?

3 Copy the wave below.

a Draw a wave that sounds louder and lower than this wave.
b Draw a wave that sounds quieter and higher than this wave.

The oscilloscope traces in diagram C show single notes with just one frequency. Most sounds do not produce such a smooth pattern. The shape of the pattern made by a sound is its **waveform**. Sounds at the same frequency sound different if they have different waveforms. For example, a harmonica sounds different from an oboe, even if both are playing the same note. We say that the **quality** of the sound produced by each instrument is different.

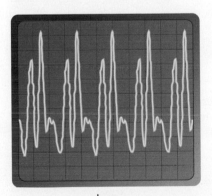
oboe

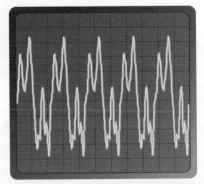
harmonica

D The waveforms of the same note played on different instruments.

4 Why does a trumpet sound different from a violin, even when they are playing the same note?

5 Draw a wave representing a sound with one frequency. Mark the amplitude on it.

6 Explain how the wave would look and sound different if it represented:
a a higher frequency
b a lower amplitude
c a note from a musical instrument.

7 Draw the waves for question **6 a** and **b** on top of the wave you drew in question **5**.

Ultrasound

By the end of this topic you should be able to:

- recall the frequencies that humans can hear
- explain what ultrasound waves are and how they are produced
- explain how ultrasound waves are used for scanning
- recall some uses of ultrasound waves

H
- work out distances from diagrams of oscilloscope traces.

Humans can hear sounds in the frequency range 20 to 20 000 Hz (or 20 kHz). Sounds with higher frequencies than this are called **ultrasound**. Some animals, such as bats, can make ultrasound which they use to detect obstacles and other objects around them. Electronic machines can also produce ultrasounds.

Ultrasound can allow us to 'see' things that cannot be detected with visible light. The most widely known use is in medical scanning, particularly for obtaining images of unborn babies.

A gel is used to stop the ultrasound just reflecting from the skin.

The probe emits and receives ultrasound waves.

The ultrasound machine detects the time between sending the pulse out and receiving the echo. The display shows where the echoes came from.

Some sound is reflected when the ultasound waves pass into a different medium, such as fat or bone.

The further down the screen, the longer the echo took to get back to the machine.

A How an ultrasound scanner works.

1 What is ultrasound?

2 Name two different things that can produce ultrasound.

3 Suggest why ultrasound is used in medical scans rather than:
  a visible light
  b X-rays.

4 Explain how an ultrasound scanner works.

Ultrasound waves can also be used for cleaning. Objects to be cleaned are put into a tank of water or other liquid, and ultrasound waves are passed through the liquid. This method is very good at cleaning delicate objects, or things with complicated shapes that cannot be cleaned in other ways.

In industry, ultrasound can be used for quality control, for example by looking for cracks inside metal objects, or for checking that a material is the correct thickness.

B Ultrasound can even be used for cleaning watches.

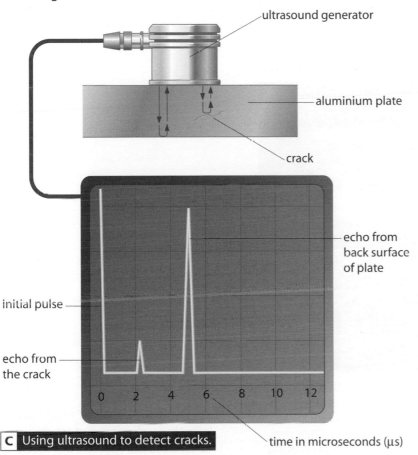

C Using ultrasound to detect cracks.

time in microseconds (μs)

H The distance between objects causing reflections can be worked out from the difference in time between the echoes:

distance = speed × time

5 Why is ultrasound useful for cleaning delicate objects?

6 Suggest how ultrasound could be used by a manufacturer to find the thickness of a metal plate.

H **7** Diagram C shows an aluminium plate being tested. The speed of sound in aluminium is 0.632 cm/μs.
  a How long (in μs) does it take for the echo to return from the crack in the plate?
  b How far has the ultrasound wave travelled in this time?
  c How far into the plate is the crack?
  d How thick is the plate?

8 **a** What frequencies could an ultrasound wave have?
  b Describe three different uses for ultrasound waves.
  H **c** Describe how an oscilloscope trace can be used to find the distances between the boundaries of different materials.

Electric motors

By the end of this topic you should be able to:

- recall that a conductor carrying an electric current may experience a force when it is in a magnetic field
- recall that a conductor does not experience a force if it is parallel to the magnetic field
- explain how to increase the size of the force and how to change its direction
- explain how the motor effect is used in simple devices.

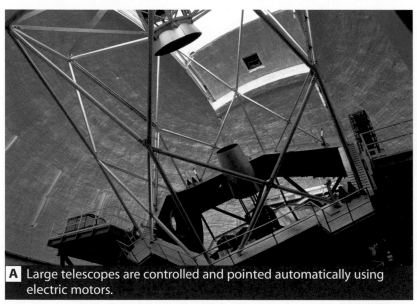

A Large telescopes are controlled and pointed automatically using electric motors.

Many machines rely on electric motors, from computers to washing machines. Electric motors work because electrical currents create **magnetic fields**.

A current flowing through a wire creates a magnetic field around it. If the wire carrying the current is placed in the magnetic field of a magnet, the two magnetic fields affect each other and the wire experiences a force. This is known as the **motor effect**.

The wire must be cossing the magnetic field for movement to occur. There is no movement if the wire is moved parallel to the magnetic field.

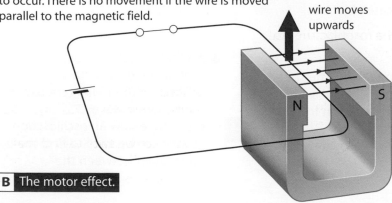

wire moves upwards

N   S

B The motor effect.

1 a Name five different machines that include electric motors.
   b What is the motor used for in each machine?

The size of the force produced can be increased by:
- increasing the current
- increasing the strength of the magnetic field.

The direction of the movement reverses if:
- the direction of the current reverses
- the direction of the magnetic field reverses.

Diagram D shows how the motor effect is used in a simple electric motor. This is a simplified drawing, as a real motor would have many more turns of wire on the coil.

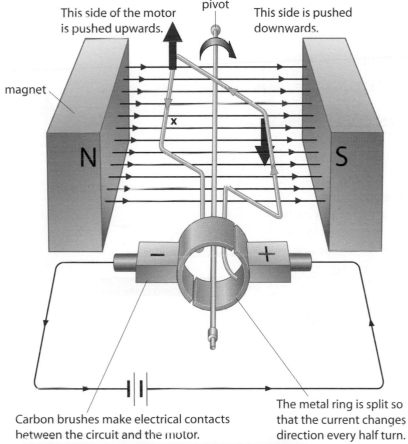

This side of the motor is pushed upwards.

pivot

This side is pushed downwards.

magnet

N

X

S

−

+

Carbon brushes make electrical contacts between the circuit and the motor.

The metal ring is split so that the current changes direction every half turn.

D Use of the motor effect in a simple electric motor.

4 Suggest why a real motor would have more turns of wire than that shown in diagram D.

H The split-ring **commutator** ensures that the force on the coil always turns it in the same direction. In diagram D, the part of the coil labelled X is moving upwards. If the current in this part of the wire was still moving in the same direction (towards us on the diagram) half a turn later, the force on it would still be upwards, and this would have the effect of trying to turn the coil in the opposite direction. The commutator ensures that the current is always flowing in the correct direction to make the coil continue to spin.

2 Look at diagram B. What will happen if:
  a the connections to the power supply are swapped over?
  b the voltage of the power supply is increased?
  c weaker magnets are used?

3 What will happen if the wire is positioned as shown in diagram C? Explain your answer.

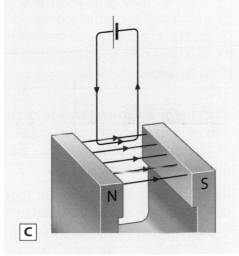

C

5 a What is the motor effect?
  b Write down two ways to make the motor effect stronger.
  c Write down two ways to make the motor effect act in the opposite direction.

Making electricity

By the end of this topic you should be able to:

- recall that a potential difference is induced if a wire 'cuts' through magnetic field lines, or if a magnet is moved into a coil of wire
- explain that a current is induced in a wire if it is part of a complete circuit
- describe how to reverse the direction of the induced current
- recall that the generator effect also occurs if the magnetic field is stationary and the coil is moved
- describe how to change the size of the induced potential difference.

Most of the electricity we use comes from the mains supply. This electricity is generated in power stations by rotating coils of wire in a magnetic field. This process is called **electromagnetic induction**.

If you move a piece of wire through a magnetic field, a potential difference is **induced** across the ends of the wire. If the wire is part of a circuit, this potential difference causes a current to flow in the wire. The wire must 'cut' the magnetic field; no potential difference is induced if the wire moves along the magnetic field lines.

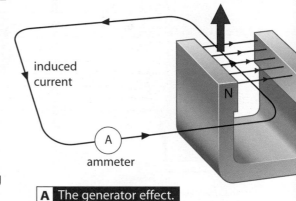

A The generator effect.

1 What is the name of the process that produces a potential difference in a generator?

2 How can we use an induced potential difference to make a current?

The induction effect is stronger if a coil of wire is used. If the direction of movement is changed, the direction of the induced current is changed. The direction of the current also depends on which way round the magnet is held.

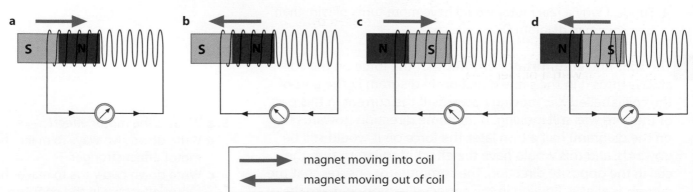

B Moving a magnet into or out of a coil of wire induces a current.

To create a continuous current, you must keep the magnet moving *relative* to the coil of wire. It does not matter whether it is the coil or the magnet that moves. You can induce a current by moving a magnet into a coil, or by moving a coil over a magnet.

The induction effect also occurs if you spin a coil in a magnetic field, because the wires in the coil cut the magnetic field as the coil spins. You get the same effect if the coil is stationary and the magnet spins.

Some bicycles have dynamos to produce electricity for the lights. Dynamos are simple generators where a magnet spins inside a coil.

C The movement of the wheel drives the dynamo. The faster the bicycle is going, the greater the induced current.

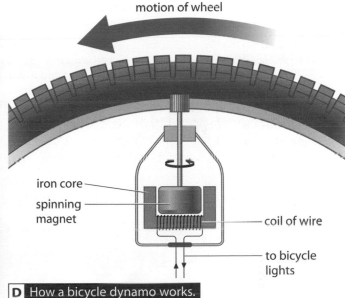

D How a bicycle dynamo works.

3 A bicycle has lights powered by a dynamo.
  a Would the lights be brighter when going uphill or downhill?
  b Explain your answer.

4 Write down some advantages and disadvantages of using a dynamo to provide electricity for bicycle lights.

A bicycle dynamo demonstrates that you can increase the potential difference induced by a generator by spinning it faster. The induced potential difference can also be increased by:
• increasing the strength of the magnetic field
• using more turns of wire on the coil
• using a coil with a bigger area.

5 Look at diagram B. Describe at least three different ways in which you could make the induced current smaller.

6 Write a short encyclopedia entry on electromagnetic induction.

Generators

By the end of this topic you should be able to:

- explain how an a.c. generator works
- explain the functions of slip rings and brushes.

A potential difference is induced if you move a wire so that it cuts through a magnetic field. Diagram A shows a simple generator that produces **alternating current** (a.c.), similar to one you could use in a school laboratory. A generator works whether a magnet spins inside a coil, or a coil spins between magnets.

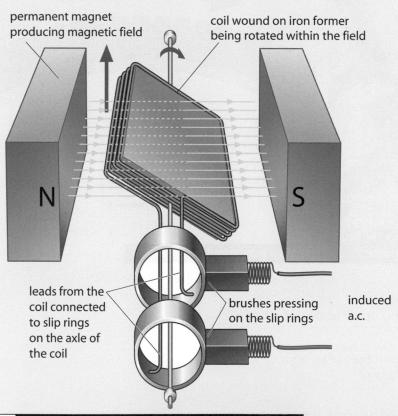

permanent magnet producing magnetic field

coil wound on iron former being rotated within the field

N   S

leads from the coil connected to slip rings on the axle of the coil

brushes pressing on the slip rings

induced a.c.

A A simple generator producing alternating current.

The **slip rings** are attached to the two ends of the wire that forms the coil. Carbon **brushes** touch the slip rings to make electrical contact between the generator and the rest of the circuit.

A potential difference is induced when the coil 'cuts through' magnetic field lines. The direction of the potential difference induced depends on how the sides of the coil are cutting through the field of the magnet. Diagrams B and C show how the potential difference varies as the coil is turned.

1 Suggest what would happen to the output of the generator if:
  a fewer turns of wire were used on the coil
  b the coil was turned faster
  c weaker magnets were used.

2 What would happen to the connecting wires if slip rings and brushes were not used?

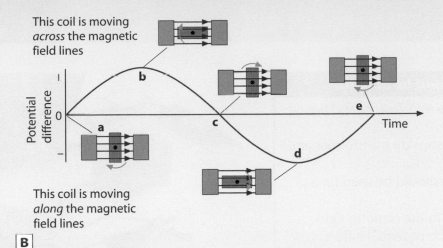

This coil is moving *across* the magnetic field lines

This coil is moving *along* the magnetic field lines

B

This part of the coil is aligned along the direction of the magnetic field, so there is no potential difference induced here.

These parts of the coil are cutting across the magnetic field, and this is where the potential difference is induced.

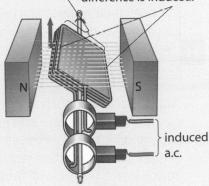

induced a.c.

C

3 a What is the difference between alternating current and direct current?
  b What can be used to produce each kind of current?

4 Explain why a rotating generator produces alternating current. Refer to the letters **a** to **e** on graph B in your answer.

The generators in power stations need to induce a very high voltage. Strong permanent magnets are very expensive, so generators often use electromagnets instead. The electromagnet spins up to 3000 times per minute inside coils of copper wire. These generators can induce potential differences of 20 000 V or more. Our mains supply is a.c. because this type of current is easier to generate.

D A generator in a power station.

5 a Why are electromagnets used in power stations instead of permanent magnets?
  b Why does the generator spin so fast?

6 Write a set of bullet points to list the key features of generators, and explain why each feature is needed.

Transformers

By the end of this topic you should be able to:

- describe the basic structure of the transformer and how it works
- explain the difference between a step-up transformer and a step-down transformer
- decide which type of transformer should be used for a particular application
- describe the uses of transformers in the National Grid
- **H** use the equation for calculating the potential differences in a transformer.

A The power supplies of devices like laptops include a transformer. The laptop needs a 20 V electricity supply.

Most appliances such as cookers, washing machines and heaters in homes and offices use the 230 V mains electricity supply directly. However, some electrical equipment needs a higher potential difference, and other equipment needs a much lower potential difference.

The size of an alternating potential difference can be changed using a **transformer**. Transformers are also used to increase the potential difference of the electricity generated by power stations.

A transformer consists of two coils of wire wound on to an iron core. The primary coil acts like an electromagnet, and magnetises the iron core. Because the direction of the current in an alternating supply keeps changing, the magnetic field produced by the coil keeps changing.

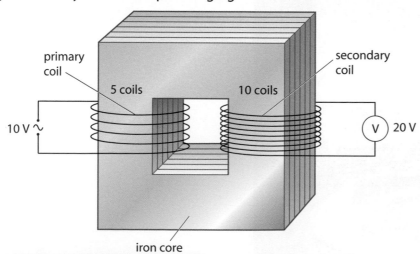

B How a transformer is constructed.

The iron core concentrates the magnetic field. The changing magnetic field in the iron core has the same effect on the secondary coil as moving a magnet in and out of the coil. An alternating potential difference is induced in the secondary coil, and a current will flow if this coil is connected to a circuit.

1 **a** Why does the direction of the magnetic field in the core keep changing?
  b What effect does this changing field have on the secondary coil?

2 Explain why a transformer does not work on direct current.

A transformer can be used to increase or decrease the potential difference of the electricity supply. A **step-up transformer** increases the potential difference, and a **step-down transformer** decreases it.

3 a In photo A, is the transformer for the laptop computer a step-up or a step-down transformer? Explain your answer.
  b In photo A, what is the potential difference across the primary coil in the laptop's transformer? Explain your answer.

H The potential difference produced by a transformer can be calculated using this equation:

$$\frac{V_p}{V_s} = \frac{N_p}{N_s}$$

where V_p and V_s are the potential differences in the primary and secondary coils, and N_p and N_s are the number of turns in the primary and secondary coils.

Example

A radio runs off the mains supply, but needs only a 23 V supply. The transformer has 100 turns of wire in the primary coil. How many turns are needed in the secondary coil?

$$\frac{V_p}{V_s} = \frac{N_p}{N_s}$$

$$\frac{230\ V}{23\ V} = \frac{100}{N_p}$$

Rearranging:

$$N_p = 100 \times \frac{23\ V}{230\ V}$$

$$= 10$$

Transformers are used in the National Grid. A power station produces alternating current at 25 kV. This is stepped up to 400 kV to be sent along power lines, since less energy is wasted when electricity is transmitted at higher potential differences. The potential difference is stepped down again to 33 kV for use in factories, and to 230 V for use in homes.

4 A transformer has an input potential difference of 230 V a.c. and there are 192 turns of wire on the primary coil. The secondary potential difference is 12 V a.c. How many turns are there on the secondary coil?

5 A transformer has 1500 turns on the primary coil and 30 000 turns on the secondary coil. What is the output potential difference for an input potential difference of 20 000 V?

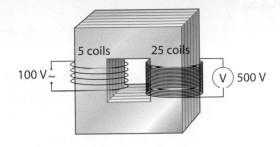

A step-up transformer has more turns in the secondary coil than in the primary coil. The potential difference across the secondary coil is greater than that across the primary coil.

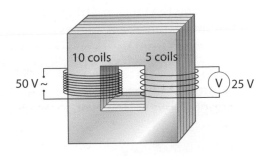

A step-down transformer has fewer turns in the secondary coil than in the primary coil. The potential difference across the secondary coil is less than that across the primary coil.

C Step-up and step-down transformers.

6 Draw a diagram of a transformer and add labels to explain how it works.

Investigative Skills Assessment

StringTunes Ltd makes and sells gadgets connected with stringed musical instruments, such as violins and guitars.

The pitch of a vibrating string depends on the length of a string, its tension (the force on it), and how heavy the string is. The 'heaviness' of the string is measured in kilograms (kg) per metre of string.

The exact pitch of each guitar string is adjusted by changing the tension. StringTunes is developing an automatic tuner that adjusts the tension on a string. A research team has been asked to investigate the effect of tension on the frequency of strings.

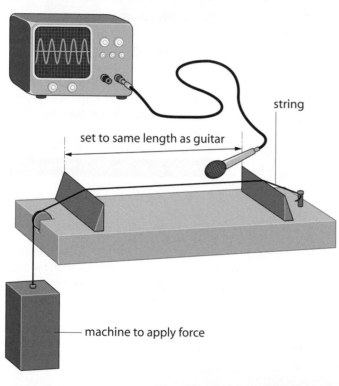

The team tested three different strings. The table shows their results.

Tension (N)	Frequency (Hz)		
	String 1	String 2	String 3
20	166	117	96
40	235	166	136
60	288	204	166
80	333	235	192
100	372	263	215
120	408	288	235

1 a What was the independent variable in this investigation? *(1 mark)*
  b Is this variable a continuous, discrete or categoric variable? *(1 mark)*
  c Name **two** variables that the team had to keep constant to make sure their investigation was a fair test. *(2 marks)*
  d What was the dependent variable? *(1 mark)*
  e Is this variable a continuous, discrete or categoric variable? *(1 mark)*

2 The team decided to test only one string of each type. This graph shows their results.

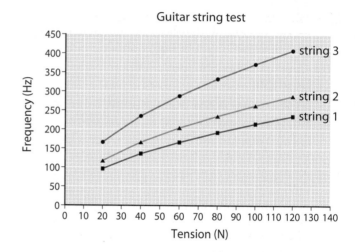

a Explain why this was not a good idea. *(1 mark)*
b Suggest how many strings of each type they should have tested. *(1 mark)*

3 ✎ The director had asked the team to find out whether the frequency of the string was proportional to its tension. Write a few sentences to the director to explain whether or not the frequency is proportional. One mark is for a clear, ordered answer. *(3 marks)*

4 What would the frequency of string 3 be if the tension is:
  a 70 N? *(1 mark)*
  b 10 N? *(1 mark)*

5 String 1 is to be the B string on a guitar, and should be tuned to a frequency of 247 Hz.
  a How can the team use the graph to work out what the tension should be for this string? *(2 marks)*
  b What should the tension be? *(1 mark)*

acceleration How quickly the velocity of a object is changing. Includes changes in direction as well as changes in speed.

alternating current Current whose direction changes many times per second.

amplitude Half the height of a wave. Related to the loudness of a sound.

angle of incidence Angle between the normal and a ray of light hitting a mirror, lens or other object.

angle of reflection Angle between the normal and a ray of light leaving a mirror, lens or other object.

black hole Body that is so dense that not even light can escape from it. Formed after a very massive star explodes.

H **brush** Carbon block that makes contact with a commutator in an electric motor or generator so that current can flow.

centre of mass Point at which you can think of all the mass of an object being concentrated.

centripetal force Force that keeps an object moving in a circle.

communications satellite Satellite used to relay telephone calls or television programmes.

H **commutator** Arrangement of split rings that allows the current to change direction in the coil of an electric motor as the coil rotates.

concave Shape of a converging mirror (where the inside of a curved shape reflects). A concave lens is thin in the middle and thicker at the edges.

converge Come together (used to describe rays of light after reflection by a mirror or refraction by a lens).

converging Coming together (of rays of light).

convex Shape of a diverging mirror (where the outside of a curved shape reflects). A convex lens is thick in the middle and thinner at the edges.

diminished Smaller.

disperse Spread out (used to describe the spreading out of the colours from white light).

diverge Spread out (used to describe rays of light after reflection by a mirror or refraction by a lens).

diverging Spreading out (of rays of light).

electromagnetic induction Process that creates a potential difference in a wire when it moves through a magnetic field, or when the magnetic field around it is changing.

elliptical Shaped like an ellipse (a squashed circle).

focal length Distance between a mirror or lens and its focus or focal point.

focus One of two 'centres' of an ellipse (plural foci). The Sun is at one focus of the elliptical orbits of the planets.

focus Point where parallel rays of light meet after being reflected by a mirror or refracted by a lens. Also called focal point.

frequency Number of waves per second.

fuse In nuclear reactions, the nuclei of two atoms fuse when they join together to form the nucleus of a new element.

galaxy Millions of stars grouped together.

geostationary orbit Orbit that takes 24 hours, so the satellite stays above the same point on the Earth all the time.

gravity Force of attraction between all masses.

hertz (Hz) Unit for frequency.

image Picture formed by a mirror or lens.

induce To cause a potential difference or current in a wire.

interface Junction between two different materials.

inverted Upside-down.

lens Shaped piece of glass or other transparent material that refracts light in particular ways.

life cycle Changes that happen to a star from its formation onwards.

magnetic field Space around a magnet where it can affect magnetic materials or other things.

medium Material that a wave travels through.

model Way of describing and explaining scientific observations.

moment Turning force.

monitoring satellite Satellite used to take pictures of the Earth to record changes in vegetation, snow cover, etc., or to record information such as temperature.

motor effect Movement of a wire carrying a current in a magnetic field.

nebular hypothesis The idea that the Solar System was formed from a swirling cloud of dust and gas.

neutron star Small, very dense star that forms after a large star explodes.

newton metre (Nm) Unit for moments.

normal Line at right angles to the surface of a mirror or lens where a ray of light hits it.

nuclear fusion reactions Reactions in which the nuclei of atoms fuse (join together) to form a different element. These are not the same as chemical reactions, where atoms do not change but only join up in different combinations.

nucleus (plural **nuclei**) Central part of an atom, containing protons and neutrons.

object Thing being looked at using a mirror or lens.

pitch How high or low a note sounds.

plane Flat.

planetary nebula Shell of dust and gas that a red giant star throws off as it starts to shrink to form a white dwarf.

polar orbit Orbit where a satellite goes over the Earth's north and south poles. Over several orbits, the satellite will eventually have flown over all parts of the Earth.

quality Property of a sound that distinguishes it from other sounds of the same frequency. The quality of a sound depends on its waveform.

radiation pressure Pressure inside a star trying to make it expand outwards, caused by high temperatures and pressures within the star.

ray diagram Diagram showing the paths of light rays, used to work out the nature of an image formed by a mirror or lens.

real image Image that light rays pass through, so that it can be seen on a screen placed at that point.

red giant Large star that forms when a normal star has used up most of its hydrogen fuel.

red supergiant Large red giant formed by stars more massive than the Sun.

refraction Change in direction when light goes from one transparent material to another.

satellite Anything that orbits around a planet or moon.

H slip ring Electrical contact between the coil in a generator and the rest of the circuit.

spectrum The seven colours that make up white light.

stable Staying the same, not changing.

star Body in space that gives off light and other kinds of radiation as a result of nuclear reactions inside it.

step-down transformer Transformer that reduces the potential difference.

step-up transformer Transformer that increases the potential difference.

supernova Explosion that happens when a massive star reaches the end of the red supergiant part of its life cycle.

transformer Device consisting of two coils on an iron core, which can change the potential difference of an alternating electricity supply.

ultrasound Sound that is too high-pitched for humans to hear, with frequencies above 20 000 Hz.

Universe All the galaxies and the space between them.

unstable Able to change easily.

upright Right way up.

velocity Speed in a particular direction. You can change velocity by changing direction without changing speed.

vibrate Move backwards and forwards quickly.

virtual image Image that light rays do not pass through; they only appear to come from the image.

waveform Shape of a wave on an oscilloscope trace.

white dwarf Small star that forms when a red giant collapses.

Assessment exercises

1 Julie has been finding the centre of mass of a piece of card.

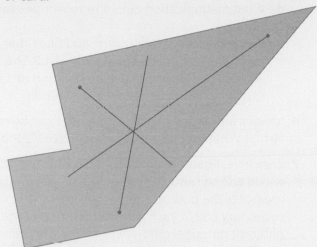

a Where is the centre of mass on the card? *(1 mark)*

b What apparatus did Julie need to find the centre of mass? *(2 marks)*

c Describe what she did with the apparatus. *(3 marks)*

d Explain why this method works. *(2 marks)*

The drawings show the results of other students in the class.

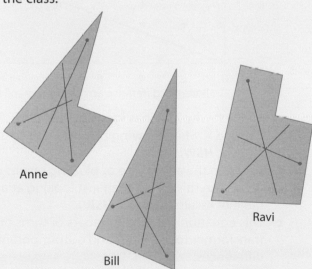

Anne

Bill

Ravi

e Who has found the location of the centre of mass to the greatest accuracy? Explain your answer. *(2 marks, **HSW**)*

f Which kind of errors have the other students made: random, systematic or zero errors? Explain your answer. *(2 marks, **HSW**)*

2 Thrills Ltd is a company that designs fairground rides. The diagram below shows part of a ride that spins passengers round in a circle.

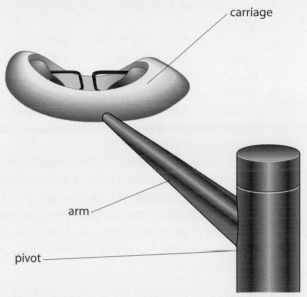

carriage

arm

pivot

a When the ride is working, the carriage spins around the central pivot at a constant speed. Explain why the carriage is accelerating as it moves, even though its speed is constant. *(1 mark)*

b The arm provides the force that keeps the carriage moving in a circle. To keep the cost down, the arm is made only as strong as it needs to be, and the following notice is displayed on the ride:

No more than 4 persons to be in the carriage

Suggest why this notice is required. *(2 marks, **HSW**)*

c Thrills Ltd also plans to make a smaller version of the ride. The carriage will still move at the same speed, but the arm will be shorter. What modification will be needed to the ride in addition to shortening the arm? Explain why this modification will be necessary. *(2 marks, **HSW**)*

3 Some early astronomers who looked at Mars thought there may be life there, because some of the features they saw looked like canals. Today we know a lot more about the surface of Mars, because spacecraft have been there and sent images and other information back to Earth. All the features seen on the surface can be explained by natural processes.

  a What hypothesis did some early astronomers make after they had observed the surface of Mars? *(1 mark, **HSW**)*

  b These early astronomers would have been able to obtain more information if more powerful telescopes had been available to them. If they had been offered such telescopes, what predictions do you think they could have made about what they might see? *(1 mark, **HSW**)*

  c Some spacecraft are put into orbit around Mars to take pictures of the surface. They become satellites of Mars. Which type of orbit would be best for a satellite orbiting Mars? Explain your answer. *(2 marks)*

4 a Which two elements were present at the beginning of the Universe? *(1 mark)*

  b Explain how atoms of the other elements have been formed. *(2 marks)*

5 Yvonne has some concave mirrors, and she wants to find which one will produce the most magnification. Some of the mirrors are more curved than others.

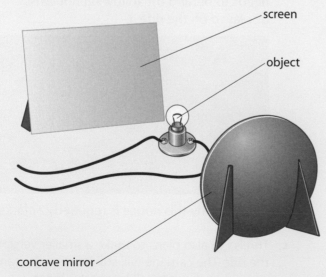

screen

object

concave mirror

  a The independent variable that Yvonne is testing is the curvature of the mirror. Which kind of variable is this? Explain your answer. *(2 marks, **HSW**)*

  b What is the dependent variable? *(1 mark, **HSW**)*

  c Draw a ray diagram for a concave mirror with a focal length of 4 cm, where the object is 6 cm from the mirror. Draw accurate rays to work out where the image is and how big it is. *(3 marks)*

  d What magnification does this mirror produce? *(1 mark)*

  e Yvonne tests another mirror, and finds that it magnifies the image by a factor of 1.5. She writes 'This mirror has a magnification of 1.5'. Explain why this is not correct. *(1 mark)*

6 Images formed by mirrors and lenses can be real or virtual. What do these two words mean? *(2 marks)*

7 Zack investigates two different transformers, to see which will be better to use with a model motor. He measures the potential difference across the secondary coil of each transformer for a range of different potential differences across the primary coil. The graph shows his results.

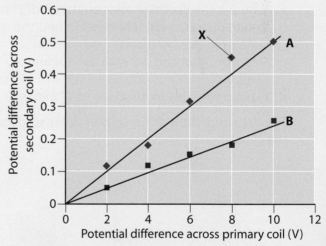

  a Suggest why Zack has ignored the point labelled X when drawing the lines on the graph. *(1 mark, **HSW**)*

  b Describe the advantage of plotting results on a graph like this, rather than just looking at a table of results. *(2 marks, **HSW**)*

  c This equation links the numbers of turns on a transformer to the input and output potential differences:

  $$\frac{V_p}{V_s} = \frac{N_p}{N_s}$$

  What is the value of $\frac{N_p}{N_s}$ for transformer A? *(2 marks)*

  d Zack wants to use the transformers to reduce the mains voltage to approximately 12 V to use with his motor. Which transformer should he use? Explain your reasoning. *(2 marks)*

8 Ultrasound can be used to detect manufacturing flaws in metal objects.

  a Explain how ultrasound can be used to do this. *(2 marks)*

  b A component is made of two strips of metal joined together in the middle, and an ultrasound probe is placed on the top surface. The oscilloscope trace shows the results of the test. The small peak represents a flaw in one of the pieces of metal.

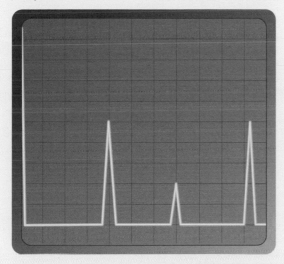

  (i) In which piece of metal is the flaw? *(1 mark)*
  (ii) What causes the other peaks? *(1 mark)*

Index

Periodic Table

Key

| relative atomic mass |
| **atomic symbol** |
| name |
| atomic (proton) number |

Example:

| 1 |
| **H** |
| hydrogen |
| 1 |

Group headers: **1 2 3 4 5 6 7 0**

1	2											3	4	5	6	7	0
1 **H** hydrogen 1																	4 **He** helium 2
7 **Li** lithium 3	9 **Be** beryllium 4											11 **B** boron 5	12 **C** carbon 6	14 **N** nitrogen 7	16 **O** oxygen 8	19 **F** fluorine 9	20 **Ne** neon 10
23 **Na** sodium 11	24 **Mg** magnesium 12											27 **Al** aluminium 13	28 **Si** silicon 14	31 **P** phosphorus 15	32 **S** sulfur 16	35.5 **Cl** chlorine 17	40 **Ar** argon 18
39 **K** potassium 19	40 **Ca** calcium 20	45 **Sc** scandium 21	48 **Ti** titanium 22	51 **V** vanadium 23	52 **Cr** chromium 24	55 **Mn** manganese 25	56 **Fe** iron 26	59 **Co** cobalt 27	59 **Ni** nickel 28	63.5 **Cu** copper 29	65 **Zn** zinc 30	70 **Ga** gallium 31	73 **Ge** germanium 32	75 **As** arsenic 33	79 **Se** selenium 34	80 **Br** bromine 35	84 **Kr** krypton 36
85 **Rb** rubidium 37	88 **Sr** strontium 38	89 **Y** yttrium 39	91 **Zr** zirconium 40	93 **Nb** niobium 41	96 **Mo** molybdenum 42	[98] **Tc** technetium 43	101 **Ru** ruthenium 44	103 **Rh** rhodium 45	106 **Pd** palladium 46	108 **Ag** silver 47	112 **Cd** cadmium 48	115 **In** indium 49	119 **Sn** tin 50	122 **Sb** antimony 51	128 **Te** tellurium 52	127 **I** iodine 53	131 **Xe** xenon 54
133 **Cs** caesium 55	137 **Ba** barium 56	139 **La*** lanthanum 57	178 **Hf** hafnium 72	181 **Ta** tantalum 73	184 **W** tungsten 74	186 **Re** rhenium 75	190 **Os** osmium 76	192 **Ir** iridium 77	195 **Pt** platinum 78	197 **Au** gold 79	201 **Hg** mercury 80	204 **Tl** thallium 81	207 **Pb** lead 82	209 **Bi** bismuth 83	[209] **Po** polonium 84	[210] **At** astatine 85	[222] **Rn** radon 86
[223] **Fr** francium 87	[226] **Ra** radium 88	[227] **Ac*** actinium 89	[261] **Rf** rutherfordium 104	[262] **Db** dubnium 105	[266] **Sg** seaborgium 106	[264] **Bh** bohrium 107	[277] **Hs** hassium 108	[268] **Mt** meitnerium 109	[271] **Ds** darmstadtium 110	[272] **Rg** roentgenium 111							

Elements with atomic numbers 112–116 have been reported but not fully authenticated.

* The Lanthanides (atomic numbers 58–71) and the Actinides (atomic numbers 90–103) have been omitted.

Cu and **Cl** have not been rounded to the nearest whole number.

Pearson Education
Edinburgh Gate
Harlow
Essex
CM20 2JE
UK
www.longman.co.uk

First published 2007

ISBN-13: 978-1-405-85563-1

Design and production	Roarrdesign
Illustration	Oxford Designers & Illustrators Ltd
Picture research	Charlotte Lippmann, Kay Altwegg
Indexer	Indexing Specialists (UK) Ltd

Printed in Scotland by Scotprint
The publisher's policy is to use paper manufactured from sustainable forests.

Front cover photos: Main image: Mari Tudor-Jones. Inset: (top) Mari Tudor-Jones (middle) NASA (bottom) Mari Tudor-Jones.

The publishers are grateful to all the copyright owners whose material appears in this book.

Every effort has been made to trace the copyright holders and we apologise in advance for any unintentional omissions. We would be pleased to insert the appropriate acknowledgement in any subsequent edition of this publication.

Acknowledgments

We are grateful to the following for permission to reproduce photographs:

(Key: b-bottom; c-centre; l-left; r-right; t-top)

Action Plus: Glyn Kirk 24; Neil Tingle 26, 134t; **Alamy Images:** 48t, 110b, 117; blickwinkel 67; Charles Bowman 93r; Digital Archive Japan 148r; Paul Doyle 116bl; Dynamic Graphics Group / Creatas 35r; David J. Green 114t, 161; Holmes Garden Photos 129t; Holt Studios International Ltd 46l; Keren Su/China Span 130; Leslie Garland Picture Library 72t; Semen Lihodeev 35l; Celia Mannings 31; Alan Novelli 116br; Otis Images 9; David Page 150; Paul Felix Photography 43; PHOTOTAKE Inc. 36r, 97t; Radius Images 129b; Runk/Schoenberger 16b; Steve Sant 134r; sciencephotos 100cl, 100l, 165, Stephen Saks Photography 47; vario images GmbH & Co.KG 46r; The Photolibrary Wales 133t; Gari Wyn Williams 86r; Colin Woodbridge 134l; Zigzag Images 148l; **Art Directors and TRIP photo Library:** Andrew Lambert Decd 97l; **Burtons Medical Equipment Ltd:** 65; **Trevor Clifford:** 66, 70, 72b, 73, 74b, 83b, 83l, 83r, 84l, 84r, 86l, 93l, 98b, 104, 105, 106bl, 106br, 106t, 107l, 107r, 110t, 114b, 120, 131, 133b, 168; Corbis: Lester Lefkowitz 167; **DK Images:** DE AGOSTINI EDITORE PICTURE LIBRARY 99t; Gary Ombler 99b; **Photograph reproduced courtesy of Eastbourne Buses Ltd:** 133l; **Mary Evans Picture Library:** 116t, 156; **Fire Testing Technology Ltd:** 119; **Food Features:** 82r, 118b, 118t; **NASA:** 127l, 127r, 141l, 141r; Goddard Space Flight Center 144l; Headquarters - GReatest Images of NASA 142b, 145; Hubble Heritage (STScI) 157; Jet Propulsion Laboratory 142t, 143; Reto Stockli with the help of Alan Nelson, under the leadership of Fritz Hasler 62; **Nuffield Book of Data:** 90; **Pearson Education:** 76b, 76t, 77bl, 77br, 77tl, 77tr, 78, 79c, 79l, 79r, 82l, 93b, 98t; Mari Tudor Jones 42, 64, 89, 91t; New Media Publications 97r; **Photographers Direct:** Darren Johnson 25; **Premier Foods:** 50, 51; **Rex Features:** Jeremy Sutton Hibbert 63; **Science Photo Library Ltd:** 102, 103, 147r; AJ PHOTO 33; AJ PHOTO / HOP AMERICAIN 30b; Andrew Lambert Photography 69b, 71, 81t, 96, 100cr, 100r; BIOPHOTO ASSOCIATES 21, 44; BSIP, RAGUET H 38; DR JEREMY BURGESS 16t, 17; CHRIS BUTLER 144r; MARTYN F. CHILLMAID 67b, 69t, 81b; EYE OF SCIENCE 14; MAURO FERMARIELLO 91b; PROF. DAVID HALL 53l; HERVE CONGE, ISM 41b; Innerspace Imaging 12; CHRIS KNAPTON 53r; G. BRAD LEWIS 162; DR KEN MACDONALD 158; MARTYN F. CHILLMAID / SCIENCE PHOTO LIBRARY 10; DR GOPAL MURTI 22; DR YORGOS NIKAS 41tr; SUSUMU NISHINAGA 23; DAVID PARKER 153; ALAIN POL, ISM 30t; ANTONIA REEVE 32; DAVID SCHARF 41t; SCIMAT 36l; ECKHARD SLAWIK 147l; SHEILA TERRY 74t; **Pictures Courtesy of Southern Water:** 61, 88

All other images © Pearson Education

Licence Agreement: *AQA GCSE Science Extension Units CD-ROM*

Warning:

This is a legally binding agreement between You (the user) and Pearson Education Limited of Edinburgh Gate, Harlow, Essex, CM20 2JE, United Kingdom ('PEL').

By retaining this Licence, any software media or accompanying written materials or carrying out any of the permitted activities You are agreeing to be bound by the terms and conditions of this Licence. If You do not agree to the terms and conditions of this Licence, do not continue to use the Disk and promptly return the entire publication (this Licence and all software, written materials, packaging and any other component received with it) with Your sales receipt to Your supplier for a full refund.

AQA GCSE Science Extension Units CD-ROM consists of copyright software and data. The copyright is owned by PEL. You only own the disk on which the software is supplied. If You do not continue to do only what You are allowed to do as contained in this Licence you will be in breach of the Licence and PEL shall have the right to terminate this Licence by written notice and take action to recover from you any damages suffered by PEL as a result of your breach.

Yes, You can:

1. use *AQA GCSE Science Extension Units CD-ROM* on your own personal computer as a single individual user;

No, You cannot:

1. copy *AQA GCSE Science Extension Units CD-ROM* (other than making one copy for back-up purposes);

2. alter *AQA GCSE Science Extension Units CD-ROM*, or in any way reverse engineer, decompile or create a derivative product from the contents of the database or any software included in it;

3. include any software data from *AQA GCSE Science Extension Units CD-ROM* in any other product or software materials;

4. rent, hire, lend or sell *AQA GCSE Science Extension Units CD-ROM*;

5. copy any part of the documentation except where specifically indicated otherwise;

6. use the software in any way not specified above without the prior written consent of PEL.

Grant of Licence:

PEL grants You, provided You only do what is allowed under the Yes, You can table above, and do nothing under the No, You cannot table above, a non-exclusive, non-transferable Licence to use *AQA GCSE Science Extension Units CD-ROM*.

The above terms and conditions of this Licence become operative when using *AQA GCSE Science Extension Units CD-ROM*.

Limited Warranty:

PEL warrants that the disk or CD-ROM on which the software is supplied is free from defects in material and workmanship in normal use for ninety (90) days from the date You receive it. This warranty is limited to You and is not transferable.

This limited warranty is void if any damage has resulted from accident, abuse, misapplication, service or modification by someone other than PEL. In no event shall PEL be liable for any damages whatsoever arising out of installation of the software, even if advised of the possibility of such damages. PEL will not be liable for any loss or damage of any nature suffered by any party as a result of reliance upon or reproduction of any errors in the content of the publication.

PEL does not warrant that the functions of the software meet Your requirements or that the media is compatible with any computer system on which it is used or that the operation of the software will be unlimited or error free. You assume responsibility for selecting the software to achieve Your intended results and for the installation of, the use of and the results obtained from the software.

PEL shall not be liable for any loss or damage of any kind (except for personal injury or death) arising from the use of *AQA GCSE Science Extension Units CD-ROM* or from errors, deficiencies or faults therein, whether such loss or damage is caused by negligence or otherwise.

The entire liability of PEL and your only remedy shall be replacement free of charge of the components that do not meet this warranty.

No information or advice (oral, written or otherwise) given by PEL or PEL's agents shall create a warranty or in any way increase the scope of this warranty.

To the extent the law permits, PEL disclaims all other warranties, either express or implied, including by way of example and not limitation, warranties of merchantability and fitness for a particular purpose in respect of *AQA GCSE Science Extension Units CD-ROM*.

Governing Law:

This Licence will be governed and construed in accordance with English law.

© Pearson Education Limited 2007